MULTIVARIATE ERROR ANALYSIS

A handbook of error propagation and calculation in many-parameter systems

MULTIVARIATE ERROR ANALYSIS

A handbook of error propagation and
calculation in many-parameter systems

A. A. CLIFFORD

Lecturer in Physical Chemistry, University of Leeds

A HALSTED PRESS BOOK

JOHN WILEY & SONS
New York—Toronto

PUBLISHED IN THE U.S.A. AND CANADA BY
HALSTED PRESS
A DIVISION OF JOHN WILEY & SONS, INC., NEW YORK

Library of Congress Cataloging in Publication Data

Clifford, A. A.
  Multivariate error analysis.

  "A Halsted Press book."
  Bibliography: p.
  1. Errors, Theory of. 2. Multivariate analysis.
I. Title.
QA275.C58   519.5'3   73–4689
ISBN 0–470–16055–1

WITH 5 TABLES AND 8 ILLUSTRATIONS

© APPLIED SCIENCE PUBLISHERS LTD 1973

Printed in Great Britain by Galliard Limited, Great Yarmouth, Norfolk, England

Preface

This handbook is intended for scientists who wish to apply the techniques of multivariate error analysis to their own problems. The basic concepts of variance, covariance and correlation coefficient are briefly explained and the equations used are derived, but the main emphasis is on describing the procedure to be followed in particular cases. The principal equations are printed between rules for easy reference and examples of the main types of calculation are given.

Multivariate error analysis is now a routine part of the calculation of crystal structures from X-ray data and is beginning to be applied to molecular-vibration calculations. It could with advantage be used in many other problems where two or more parameters are involved. This is especially so in complex problems such as those involving interferometric spectroscopy and certain aspects of nuclear magnetic resonance spectroscopy. But, even with a simple two-parameter equation like the Arrhenius equation, knowledge of the covariance of the two parameters is important, particularly in subsequent calculations, as is shown in the book. And, now that so much data is processed by computer, a multivariate error analysis can be a relatively painless addition to a calculation. In Appendix B, computer procedures are given in both Algol and Fortran, which can be included in readers' programmes.

The theories of multivariate error analysis and of least-squares analysis overlap considerably and consequently least-squares is referred to and the main equations and procedures given. However, least-squares may not be the best parameter-fitting method, particularly in complex non-linear problems. Consequently, the subject is only dealt with briefly as a side issue in this book. Parameter-fitting with speed and efficiency is now a highly technical business in the field of computer programming and a more detailed discussion of it is beyond the scope of the present volume.

Contents

CHAPTER 1

Introduction: Variance and covariance

1.1 INTRODUCTION

Everyone recognises the importance of error calculation to the research scientist. When only one parameter is being obtained from an experiment, crude methods of calculation suffice to obtain an estimate of the uncertainty of the result and the reader will be more than familiar with the simple procedures normally used. However, in many research problems, a number of parameters are obtained simultaneously from an equal or greater number of experimental results. In these cases more formal methods must be used to obtain correct estimates of the uncertainties in the parameters. These methods come under the heading of multivariate error analysis.

The purpose of this book is to present multivariate error analysis to the research scientist in an easily digestible form. The material presented is already available in more advanced books on statistics, which are listed in the bibliography. Here discussion of the general principles will be limited to the minimum needed to be able to use knowledgeably the equations that are derived. The main emphasis is on outlining the procedures to be used in various situations. The principal equations are printed between rules for easy reference.

Central to the methods of multivariate error analysis are the concepts of variance and covariance. These are explained in this chapter. Most readers will be familiar with the idea of variance, but the covariance and the related quantity, the correlation coefficient, will probably be new to readers of this introductory book. The covariance, in the context of error analysis, is a measure of how much the errors in two quantities are correlated. For example, if the covariance is high and positive, it indicates that the factor which is causing one quantity to be assigned, say, a value higher than the

1

true value is also causing the other quantity to be assigned too high a value. It is neglect of covariance in a many-parameter problem which causes the calculation of errors by less sophisticated methods to be incorrect. In this book we will try to show the importance of the covariance in even two-parameter problems.

The methods of multivariate error analysis and the methods of least-squares and of least-squares refinement have much of their theory in common. At one time a book of this sort would have included both topics side by side. Least-squares is useful for the relatively small number of problems that arise where the observables and parameters are linearly related, but for the majority of problems, which are non-linear, the method of least-squares refinement suffers from a number of disadvantages. There are now a number of function minimisation procedures,* available as library routines on most large computer systems, which can fit parameters to experimental data quickly and efficiently using the *principle* of least-squares. Least-squares refinement is therefore discussed briefly in this book and is only included for completeness and because many of the equations are similar. Readers may find the method useful for simple problems, but if difficulties are encountered, other methods should be investigated.

Before discussing the layout of the book, it is first necessary to describe how the terms *observable* and *parameter* are used in it. In general they have their normal meanings, *i.e.* the observables are the experimental observables, but they may either be the experimental measurements themselves or quantities derived from the measurements. Except when calculating errors in predicted observables, they are the starting-point of the error procedure; the outcome being errors in the parameters. However, the parameters from one calculation can become the observables in another calculation. For example, the frequencies in a microwave spectrum could be used as observables to calculate the moments of inertia of a molecule as parameters. The moments of inertia could then be used as observables to calculate the bond distances in the molecule as parameters. The situation should be clear in particular cases.

After this initial chapter, the book falls into two halves. Chapters 2 and 3 deal with problems in which there are only two parameters, while Chapters 4 and 5 treat the general multivariate error problem. This separation is to a certain extent rather arbitrary and arises

---

* See J. Kowalik and M. R. Osborne, *Methods for Unconstrained Optimisation Problems*, Chapter 4, Least squares problems, Elsevier, New York, 1968.

because the equations for the two-parameter problem can be written in terms of simple algebra, whereas the many-parameter equations have to be written in matrix notation. Those with a two-parameter problem need therefore read no further than Chapter 3. Those with a many-parameter problem will gain by reading through Chapters 2 and 3, since the procedures are easier to understand in the two-parameter problem and also some of the basic concepts are explained further there.

The book is then divided into chapters on the following basis. Chapters 2 and 4 describe error analysis in cases where the parameters are calculated from the same number of observables. The errors in the parameters have then to be obtained from those in the observables by *propagation*. Chapters 3 and 5 describe error analysis in cases where a number of parameters are calculated from a greater number of observables; *i.e.* the parameters are overdetermined. In these cases, errors in the parameters can be obtained either by *propagation* from the errors in the observables, or by *calculation* from the differences between the experimental values of the observables and values back-calculated from the parameters. Both procedures are described separately in Chapters 3 and 5.

Occasionally we will need to use errors in parameters to calculate errors in predicted observables or further parameters either greater or fewer in number than the original parameters. When the number is greater, then the observables or parameters will not all be independent quantities. When the number is fewer, we must ensure that this is not a case where the parameters are overdetermined by the observables: all the original parameters must be necessary to obtain the derived quantities. In these cases, the propagation methods of Chapters 2 and 4 are appropriate and there are sections in these chapters on this.

Except in the case just mentioned, the parameters should always be an independent set. That is, it should not be possible for any of them to be calculated from any combination of the others. It is not possible, in one stage, to obtain errors in a non-independent set of parameters, if the parameters are overdetermined. The analysis must be done in the following two steps. Firstly the errors in any independent set of parameters must be obtained using the methods of Chapters 3 and 5. Then the errors can be propagated to the larger non-independent set using the methods given at the ends of Chapters 2 and 4.

In Appendix B two computer procedures or subroutines, called *errprop* and *errcalc*, are given in both Algol and Fortran, which can be used to carry out any of the error analyses covered in this book. *Errprop* will do any of the computations of Chapters 2 and 4 and also the error propagation procedures of Chapters 3 and 5. *Errcalc* will do the error calculation procedures of Chapters 3 and 5.

The notation used has been kept deliberately simple, so that some of the distinctions made in the usual treatment of this subject are not observed here. The bar, *e.g.* in $\bar{x}_i$, is used to indicate the mean value of a very large number of observations, *i.e.* the population mean or what one might call the true value. x_i indicates the measured value of an observable and y_i the calculated value of a parameter, or in the case of an overdetermined parameter, the expectation value of the parameter, obtained using the principle of least-squares.

1.2 VARIANCE

The *variance* of a quantity is a concept which is easily grasped, since it is identical to the square of the familiar *standard deviation*. To define we imagine that we can obtain an observable (or parameter), x, a very large number of times and obtain N values ${}^i x$, where N is a number approaching infinity. The *mean*, $\bar{x}$, is then defined by

$$\bar{x} = \frac{1}{N} \sum_{i=1}^{N} {}^i x \qquad (1.2\text{-}1)$$

The *variance* of x, var(x), is defined as the mean squared deviation of x from $\bar{x}$ and is therefore given by

$$\text{var}(x) = \frac{1}{N} \sum_{i=1}^{N} ({}^i x - \bar{x})^2 \qquad (1.2\text{-}2)$$

The *standard deviation* of x, $\sigma(x)$, as mentioned earlier, is defined to be the positive root of

$$\sigma^2(x) = \text{var}(x) \qquad (1.2\text{-}3)$$

If the reader has come across these terms already, it is likely he has done so in connection with the normal or Gaussian distribution. It will often be helpful to think of the equations in this book in terms of the normal distribution and occasionally this will be done in the text. The theory given here is, however, independent of the distribution of the observables or parameters.

1.3 ESTIMATION OF THE VARIANCE OF OBSERVABLES

In practice a finite and comparatively small number of measurements of x are made and an estimate of the variance must be used instead of the exact result from eqn. (1.2-2). The least sophisticated, but probably the most common method is to make one measurement of x and then to make a guesstimate of $\sigma(x)$ from knowledge of previous measurements, the known reliability of the experimental method, the manufacturer's specifications of the apparatus, noise on an oscilloscope or pen recorder, etc. These methods if used properly are quite an acceptable way of starting a multivariate error calculation. They depend so much on the particular experiment that discussion here has to be restricted. It is important, however, to bear in mind the difference between the variance of individual results and the variance of an average value. This difference is discussed later in the section and means, for example, that the centre line of a noisy pen-recorder trace probably has a much smaller variance than the mean-squared pen excursions. Due allowance must, of course, be made for possible 'consistent errors'.

A better estimate of the variance can be obtained by making a small number, n, measurements of x. The equations then used are familiar and will be stated rather than proved. From these measurements an average value, $\langle x \rangle$, can be obtained, where

$$\langle x \rangle = \frac{1}{n} \sum_{i=1}^{n} {}^i x \qquad (1.3\text{-}1)$$

This average, $\langle x \rangle$, will not be the same number as the true mean, $\bar{x}$, since insufficient measurements of x have been made. Similarly, insufficient values have been obtained to use eqn. (1.2-2) for var(x). An estimate of var(x) is, however, given by the following well-known formula*

$$\text{var}(x) \approx \frac{1}{n-1} \sum_{i=1}^{n} ({}^i x - \langle x \rangle)^2 \qquad (1.3\text{-}2)$$

Having made several measurements, we will want to use $\langle x \rangle$, the best estimate of $\bar{x}$, in the subsequent calculation rather than a single

---

* $n - 1$ rather than n replaces N in eqn. (1.2-2). If n is fairly large then it can be used instead of $n - 1$ without much loss of accuracy. The formula is derived in many books including Margenau, H. and Murphy, G. M. *The Mathematics of Physics and Chemistry*, van Nostrand, New York, 1956, p. 507.

measurement $^i x$. The variance of the average, $\mathrm{var}(\langle x \rangle)$, is therefore required for the error calculation. It can readily be shown that

$$\mathrm{var}(\langle x \rangle) = \frac{1}{n}\,\mathrm{var}(x) \qquad\qquad (1.3\text{-}3)$$

Combining eqns. (1.3-2) and (1.3-3) we obtain:

Estimation of the variance and the standard deviation of an average of a number of measurements of an observable

---

$$\mathrm{var}(\langle x \rangle) = \frac{1}{n(n-1)} \sum_{i=1}^{n} (^i x - \langle x \rangle)^2$$

$$\sigma(\langle x \rangle) = [\mathrm{var}(\langle x \rangle)]^{\frac{1}{2}} \qquad\qquad (1.3\text{-}4)$$

The accuracy with which $\mathrm{var}(\langle x \rangle)$ is estimated by the above equations depends on the number, n, of observations made and also the distribution of the particular observable. For a normal or Gaussian distribution, six observations are more than likely to give an estimate of $\mathrm{var}(\langle x \rangle)$ to within 10 per cent of the true value. This would therefore be a good rule to follow when the distribution is not known but is likely to be nearly normal.

In subsequent calculations the angular brackets around x will be dropped and the average value can be treated as a single observation with appropriate variance and standard deviation.

Before leaving this section a word should be said about 'consistent errors'. Readers will no doubt be familiar with the term; it needs no explanation to most scientists. It should perhaps be mentioned that we really mean a consistent error whose value and sign are unknown. Known consistent errors are routinely corrected for after measurement. If the amount of the consistent error is not known but the sign is known, then the correct procedure is to adjust the observable by half the likely consistent error. The estimate of the consistent error can then be halved.

In terms of the concepts so far discussed, the consistent error has no meaning. As it cannot be estimated by repeated measurement, the procedure of the intelligent guess has to be resorted to. The variance of the observable should then be increased appropriately. For example, if a consistent error of 0·2 is suspected, $(0·2)^2 = 0·04$ should be added to the variance.

An example of the estimation of the standard deviation is given in Section 1.6.

1.4 COVARIANCE AND THE CORRELATION COEFFICIENT

The *covariance* and the *correlation coefficient* are important if the errors in two observables or parameters arise from the same physical cause. Thus if two quantities are measured completely independently, then the covariance and the correlation coefficient will both be zero. For this to be strictly true, even the physical constants used in trivial conversion of the raw measurements to observables (*e.g.* millimetres of mercury into pressure) must be different for each observable and completely independent. These rigorous conditions are rarely met in practice. However, the errors in physical constants such as Planck's or Boltzmann's constants are usually much smaller than other errors and can be neglected.

Conversely, if the measurements are connected physically in some way, both the covariance and the correlation coefficient will be nonzero. The effect of this physical connection could be, for example, that, when the error in one quantity is positive, then the error in the other quantity is more likely to be positive than negative. In this case both the covariance and the correlation coefficient will be positive. On the other hand, it can also happen that, when the error in one quantity is positive, the error in the other quantity is more likely to be negative than positive. Then the covariance and the correlation coefficient will both be negative.* The linguistics of the two terms then becomes clear. Covariance is a measure of the way in which the two observables or parameters vary together and the term correlation coefficient refers to the extent to which the two errors are correlated.

The covariance is defined in the following way. We imagine that we have the time to make an extremely large number, N, approaching infinity, of connected measurements of two quantities x_1 and x_2. By connected we mean here made in the same relation to one another as they would be in a single experiment, *e.g.* at the same time, or in

---

* These generalisations, made for explanatory purposes, may not always be true for certain unusual distributions.

the same run, etc. Then the covariance of x_1 and x_2, $\text{cov}(x_1, x_2)$, is defined by

$$\text{cov}(x_1, x_2) = \frac{1}{N} \sum_{i=1}^{N} ({}^i x_1 - \bar{x}_1)({}^i x_2 - \bar{x}_2) \qquad (1.4\text{-}1)$$

If, in a particular problem, there are more than two quantities involved, each pair, *e.g.* x_j and x_k, will have a covariance:

$$\text{cov}(x_j, x_k) = \frac{1}{N} \sum_{i=1}^{N} ({}^i x_j - \bar{x}_j)({}^i x_k - \bar{x}_k) \qquad (1.4\text{-}2)$$

The variance can thus be seen to be a special case of the covariance when $j = k$.

That the covariance is zero when the quantities are physically independent can be argued as follows. Consider a very small range of values of x_1. Since a nearly infinite number of pairs of measurements have been made, a nearly infinite number of measurements will fall in this small range of x_1. Measurements in this range will be paired with measurements of x_2 which will cover the whole range of x_2 in a random way, as x_2 is independent of x_1. The sum

$$\sum ({}^i x_1 - \bar{x}_1)({}^i x_2 - \bar{x}_2)$$

taken over the small range of x_1 will therefore be zero, as the first factor is a constant for all terms and the sum of the second factors is zero by the definition of $\bar{x}_2$. This will be true for any small range of x_1, and thus the covariance by definition will be zero for the two physically independent quantities. The inverse of this assertion, it should perhaps be mentioned, is not necessarily true. Zero covariance does not ensure independence.

The *correlation coefficient* is defined in terms of the covariance, thus:

$$\rho(x_i, x_j) = \frac{\text{cov}(x_i, x_j)}{\sigma(x_i)\sigma(x_j)} \qquad (1.4\text{-}3)$$

The correlation coefficient must lie in the range of -1 to $+1$ (by Schwarz's inequality). In the trivial case when $i = j$, $\rho = 1$, *i.e.* the correlation coefficient of the error of a quantity with itself is unity. As with the covariance, the correlation coefficient is zero for two independently measured quantities. The correlation coefficient in other cases is closely related to the probability distribution of pairs of quantities and this will be demonstrated by example in Section 1.6 and also given a geometrical interpretation for the normal distribution in Section 2.3.

The usefulness of the correlation coefficient in fully understanding the error situation of two quantities is apparent. More importantly, the correlation coefficient greatly affects the way in which errors propagate. Suppose a parameter is calculated from two observables. And suppose, for example, that positive errors in the observables both cause the calculated value of the parameter to be higher than the true value. If the errors in the observables are uncorrelated, the errors will add in a random way to produce an error in the parameter. If there is a positive correlation coefficient between the two observable errors, then the errors will reinforce to give a larger error in the parameter. If the correlation coefficient is negative, the errors will cancel to a certain extent to reduce the error in the parameter. Rigorous error calculation without taking into account the correlation coefficient is impossible and its effect is sometimes very large.

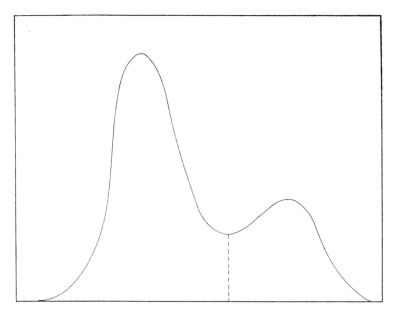

FIG. 1.1 Arbitrary separation of the areas of two peaks on a spectrum.

1.5 ESTIMATION OF THE CORRELATION COEFFICIENT OF OBSERVABLES

In many experiments it will be possible to assert that the observables have been independently measured and that the correlation coefficient is zero. Indeed the experiments may have been designed, consciously or unconsciously, to this end. For example, when measuring points on a function traced on a pen recorder, care may have been taken not to measure them more closely than about five times the amplifier time-constant.

Equally obviously, in a few cases, the correlation coefficient will be $+1$ or -1. An example of this is given in Fig. 1.1, where the areas of two overlapping peaks on a spectrum have to be assigned values by rather arbitrary separation. If the separation is erroneous, the error in the area of one peak will be equal and opposite to the error in the other peak, if this separation is by far the major source of error. The correlation coefficient will therefore be -1.

In other cases a small number of measurements of pairs of values can be made and the covariance estimated in much the same way as the variance is estimated:

$$\text{cov}(x_j, x_k) \approx \frac{1}{n-1} \sum_{i=1}^{n} (^i x_j - \langle x_j \rangle)(^i x_k - \langle x_k \rangle) \qquad (1.5\text{-}1)$$

The correlation coefficient is therefore given by the formula:

Estimation of the correlation coefficient

$$\rho(x_j, x_k) \approx \frac{\displaystyle\sum_{i=1}^{n} (^i x_j - \langle x_j \rangle)(^i x_k - \langle x_k \rangle)}{\left[\displaystyle\sum_{i=1}^{n} (^i x_j - \langle x_j \rangle)^2 \sum_{i=1}^{n} (^i x_k - \langle x_k \rangle)^2\right]^{\frac{1}{2}}} \qquad (1.5\text{-}2)$$

The advantage of dealing with the correlation coefficient here is that there is no distinction between its value for individual pairs of values and for the average values, as there is for the variance and covariance. In fact, although in deriving the equations the variance and covariance are the important basic quantities, in practical calculations one deals with the standard deviation and correlation coefficient.

The reliability of the estimate of ρ also depends on n, the number of observations. Also if n is small the numerical value of ρ obtained will tend to be low on average. However, as before, measurement of six pairs of values will give an estimate of ρ which is likely to be within 10 per cent of the true value.

1.6 ESTIMATION OF STANDARD DEVIATION AND CORRELATION COEFFICIENT: EXAMPLE

The example given here is the simultaneous measurement of the parallel resistance, R, and capacitance, C, of an electrical circuit, using an a.c. bridge. For those not familiar with the measurement, the circuit is connected to the bridge and two dials are adjusted to give a minimum reading on a meter. The position of one of the dials then gives the resistance and that of the other the capacitance. Simply from handling the bridge, one would suspect that the errors in these two quantities were correlated because, if one of the dials is set off its

TABLE 1.1

CALCULATION OF STANDARD DEVIATION AND CORRELATION
COEFFICIENT

$R(\Omega)$	$C(\text{nF})$	$R - \langle R \rangle$	$C - \langle C \rangle$	$(R - \langle R \rangle)^2$	$(C - \langle C \rangle)^2$	$(R - \langle R \rangle) \times (C - \langle C \rangle)$
1 169	1 029·5	+0·6	−0·25	0·36	0·062 5	−0·15
1 168	1 030·5	−0·4	+0·75	0·16	0·562 5	−0·30
1 170	1 028·0	+1 6	−1·75	2·56	3·062 5	−2·80
1 168	1 029·5	−0·4	−0·25	0·16	0·062 5	+0·10
1 167	1 030 0	−1·4	+0·25	1·96	0·062 5	−0·35
1 170	1 029·0	+1·6	−0·75	2·56	0·562 5	−1·20
1 168	1 030·5	−0·4	+0·75	0·16	0·562 5	−0·30
1 169	1 029·5	+0·6	−0·25	0·36	0·062 5	−0·15
1 168	1 030·0	−0·4	+0·25	0·16	0·062 5	−0·10
1 167	1 031·0	−1·4	+1·25	1·96	1·562 5	−1·75
1 169	1 028·5	+0·6	−1·25	0·36	1·562 5	−0·75
1 168	1 031·0	−0·4	+1·25	0·16	1·562 5	−0·50
14 021	12 357·0	—	—	10·92	9·75	−8·25

minimum point, the needle can be brought almost as low again by adjusting the other dial. In deference to manufacturers of this type of equipment, it should be pointed out that it is possible to make measurements more accurately than is done in this example. Here we wish to emphasise the effect of errors and so the bridge was used deliberately disadvantageously.

Twelve pairs of values of R and C, obtained experimentally, are given in the first two columns of Table 1.1. The first step is to calculate the averages $\langle R \rangle$ and $\langle C \rangle$. The sums of R and C are given at the base of the columns and these give the values:

$$\langle R \rangle = 1168 \cdot 4 \quad \text{and} \quad \langle C \rangle = 1029 \cdot 75$$

From these averages, the values of $(R - \langle R \rangle)$ and $(C - \langle C \rangle)$ can be calculated and these are shown in the third and fourth columns. These quantities are then squared and entered in the fifth and sixth columns. Also the cross-products $(R - \langle R \rangle)(C - \langle C \rangle)$ are calculated and appear in the seventh column. The fifth, sixth and seventh columns are then summed, the sums being shown at the base of the columns. These sums can then be used in eqns. (1.3-4) and (1.5-2) to obtain the standard deviations and correlation coefficient. The

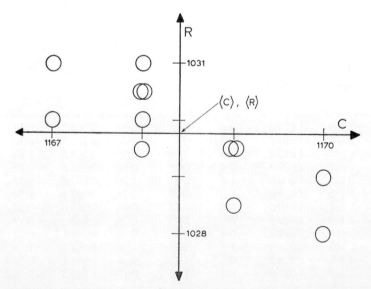

FIG. 1.2 The correlation of errors in resistance and capacitance measured by an a.c. bridge.

final results are:

$$\sigma(\langle R \rangle) = 0.27$$

$$\sigma(\langle C \rangle) = 0.29$$

and

$$\rho(R, C) = \rho(\langle R \rangle, \langle C \rangle) = -0.64$$

The values of R and C are also shown plotted against one another in Fig. 1.2. Apart from the general scatter of results, a spreading of the points from the top-left to the bottom-right of the diagram can be seen. This indicates negative correlation between the errors in R and C, which is reflected in the value of -0.64 for the correlation coefficient.

1.7 PARTIAL DERIVATIVES: AVAILABILITY AND USE

In all subsequent expressions, x_i will always be used to denote an observable and y_j a parameter. In order to propagate or calculate errors, one of the sets of derivatives $(\partial y_i/\partial x_j)$ or $(\partial x_i/\partial y_j)$ must be used. Which set is required will depend on the particular problem and in this section we consider the availability of these derivatives and their use in different cases.

It will usually be possible to write an expression for the observables, x_i, in terms of the parameters, y_j

$$x_i \equiv x_i(y_1, y_2, \ldots) \tag{1.7-1}$$

In these cases it will be possible to write expressions for the $(\partial x_i/\partial y_j)$ derivatives and thus it will be easy to calculate their numerical values in particular cases.

In fewer cases, it will be possible to also write expressions for the parameters in terms of the observables,

$$y_i \equiv y_i(x_1, x_2, \ldots) \tag{1.7-2}$$

and in these cases algebraic expressions for the $(\partial y_i/\partial x_j)$ derivatives will be available.

And in a few cases it will not be possible to write even expressions of the form of (1.7-1). For example, the observable might be the solution of a differential equation in which the parameters appear as constants and solution may only be possible by numerical methods. In these cases the derivatives can be estimated by the difference method. Each of the parameters is changed in turn by a small amount and the change in each observable is noted and used to estimate the appropriate derivative. The amount of the change is kept as small as possible so that the differences give the derivatives as accurately as possible, but it is not made so small that rounding errors become important. Tests of the effect of the size of the changes are desirable in some cases.

To sum up: the derivatives $(\partial x_i/\partial y_j)$ are usually available by algebra, but sometimes must be obtained by difference. The derivatives $(\partial y_i/\partial x_j)$ can sometimes also be readily calculated.

However, it has also to be borne in mind that, if either the observables or the parameters are not all independent, then one of the sets of derivatives will not be defined. As a result of this and also the availability criterion, the derivatives to be used will depend on the problem in hand. The consequent rules can be summarised as follows. When the parameters are overdetermined by a greater number of observables, the derivatives $(\partial x_i/\partial y_j)$ are used. When there are the same number of parameters as observables, then either set of derivatives may be used, but the $(\partial y_i/\partial x_j)$ derivatives are more convenient, so they are used if available. For propagating errors in predicted observables the $(\partial x_i/\partial y_j)$ must be used. For propagating errors to non-independent parameters the $(\partial y_i/\partial x_j)$ must be used.

1.8 THE LINEAR ASSUMPTION

Throughout the derivations in later chapters, it is assumed that, whatever the functional relationship between the observables and parameters, this can be approximated by a linear relationship and that this approximation is reasonably accurate over the range of the errors. This assumption will often be valid, but should be considered for every problem and checked numerically if there is any doubt. Doubtful situations arise when the function is very non-linear and when the linear terms are small. Caution is therefore necessary when any observable or parameter is near a maximum or minimum value or near a point of inflexion. And functions which have discontinuities or discontinuous derivatives in the region of the errors require special consideration.

Mathematically, the approximation rests on the validity of the Taylor expansion of each parameter around the mean values of the observables and moreover on the fact that the linear terms in the expansion are the most significant in the error region. This boils down to an assumption that, for every observable-parameter pair:

$$\frac{\partial y_i}{\partial x_j} \gg \frac{\partial^2 y_i}{\partial x_j^2} \sigma(x_j) + \frac{\partial^3 y_i}{\partial x_j^3} \sigma^2(x_j) + \frac{\partial^4 y_i}{\partial x_j^4} \sigma^3(x_j) + \cdots \qquad (1.8\text{-}1)$$

The linear assumption can therefore be checked using this inequality. If it is not valid, then the errors in the parameters will depend significantly on the second and higher derivatives and on the form of the observable distribution function and the error analysis outlined in this manual will not be valid.

CHAPTER 2

Error propagation from two observables to two parameters

In this chapter the propagation of errors from two observables, x_1 and x_2, to two parameters, y_1 and y_2, is discussed. Firstly, the common situation where the observables have errors that are uncorrelated is dealt with. Later, equations are developed for the situation where the correlation coefficient for the observables, $\rho(x_1, x_2)$ is non-zero. Finally, propagation to predicted observables and non-independent parameters is discussed.

2.1 LINEAR RELATIONSHIPS

To simplify notation, difference quantities are defined for the observables,

$$\delta x_1 = x_1 - \bar{x}_1$$

and

$$\delta x_2 = x_2 - \bar{x}_2 \tag{2.1-1}$$

and also for the parameters

$$\delta y_1 = y_1 - \bar{y}_1$$

and

$$\delta y_2 = y_2 - \bar{y}_2 \tag{2.1-2}$$

If a Taylor expansion is made for the observables and second and higher terms neglected, the resulting expressions can be written in terms of these differences quantities as follows:

$$\delta x_1 = \frac{\partial x_1}{\partial y_1} \cdot \delta y_1 + \frac{\partial x_1}{\partial y_2} \cdot \delta y_2$$

$$\delta x_2 = \frac{\partial x_2}{\partial y_1} \cdot \delta y_1 + \frac{\partial x_2}{\partial y_2} \cdot \delta y_2 \tag{2.1-3}$$

Similar expressions can also be written for the parameter differences:

$$\delta y_1 = \frac{\partial y_1}{\partial x_1} \cdot \delta x_1 + \frac{\partial y_1}{\partial x_2} \cdot \delta x_2$$

$$\delta y_2 = \frac{\partial y_2}{\partial x_1} \cdot \delta x_1 + \frac{\partial y_2}{\partial x_2} \cdot \delta x_2 \qquad (2.1\text{-}4)$$

Actually it is eqns. (2.1-4) that are used directly in calculating the parameter errors. However, as mentioned in Section 1.7, these derivatives may not be directly available. They can, however, be calculated from the other set of derivatives by solving eqns. (2.1-3):

$$\frac{\partial y_1}{\partial x_1} = \frac{(\partial x_2/\partial y_2)}{J} \qquad \frac{\partial y_1}{\partial x_2} = -\frac{(\partial x_1/\partial y_2)}{J}$$

$$\frac{\partial y_2}{\partial x_1} = -\frac{(\partial x_2/\partial y_1)}{J} \qquad \frac{\partial y_2}{\partial x_2} = \frac{(\partial x_1/\partial y_1)}{J} \qquad (2.1\text{-}5)$$

where J is known as the Jacobian determinant, given by:

$$J = \begin{vmatrix} \dfrac{\partial x_1}{\partial y_1} & \dfrac{\partial x_1}{\partial y_2} \\[2mm] \dfrac{\partial x_2}{\partial y_1} & \dfrac{\partial x_2}{\partial y_2} \end{vmatrix} \qquad (2.1\text{-}6)$$

In this chapter, it is assumed that there are zero or negligible errors in these derivatives. If this is not so, the methods of Section 4.7 must be used.

2.2 TWO UNCORRELATED OBSERVABLES

In this section expressions are derived for the variances $\text{var}(y_1)$ and $\text{var}(y_2)$ and the covariance $\text{cov}(y_1, y_2)$ in terms of the variances $\text{var}(x_1)$ and $\text{var}(x_2)$. The calculation starts with eqn. (1.2-2) for $\text{var}(y_1)$:

$$\text{var}(y_1) = \frac{1}{N}\sum_{i=1}^{N}({}^iy_1 - \bar{y}_1)^2 = \frac{1}{N}\sum_{i=1}^{N}({}^i\delta y_1)^2$$

$$= \frac{1}{N}\sum_{i=1}^{N}\left[\frac{\partial y_1}{\partial x_1}\cdot{}^i\delta x_1 + \frac{\partial y_1}{\partial x_2}\cdot{}^i\delta x_2\right]^2$$

$$= \frac{1}{N}\left(\frac{\partial y_1}{\partial x_1}\right)^2\sum_{i=1}^{N}({}^i\delta x_1)^2 + \frac{1}{N}\left(\frac{\partial y_1}{\partial x_2}\right)^2\sum_{i=1}^{N}({}^i\delta x_2)^2$$

$$+ \frac{2}{N}\left(\frac{\partial y_1}{\partial x_1}\cdot\frac{\partial y_1}{\partial x_2}\right)\sum_{i=1}^{N}({}^i\delta x_1)({}^i\delta x_2)$$

The last term is proportional to $\text{cov}(x_1, x_2)$ and is therefore zero, since the observables are uncorrelated. The first two terms are proportional to $\text{var}(x_1)$ and $\text{var}(x_2)$ respectively. Hence:

$$\text{var}(y_1) = \left(\frac{\partial y_1}{\partial x_1}\right)^2\text{var}(x_1) + \left(\frac{\partial y_1}{\partial x_2}\right)^2\text{var}(x_2) \qquad (2.2\text{-}1)$$

Similarly:

$$\text{var}(y_2) = \left(\frac{\partial y_2}{\partial x_1}\right)^2\text{var}(x_1) + \left(\frac{\partial y_2}{\partial x_2}\right)^2\text{var}(x_2) \qquad (2.2\text{-}2)$$

The covariance $\text{cov}(y_1, y_2)$ is calculated by similar methods:

$$\text{cov}(y_1, y_2) = \frac{1}{N}\sum_{i=1}^{N}({}^i\delta y_1)({}^i\delta y_2)$$

$$= \frac{1}{N}\sum_{i=1}^{N}\left[\frac{\partial y_1}{\partial x_1}\cdot{}^i\delta x_1 + \frac{\partial y_1}{\partial x_2}\cdot{}^i\delta x_2\right]$$

$$\times \left[\frac{\partial y_2}{\partial x_1}\cdot{}^i\delta x_1 + \frac{\partial y_2}{\partial x_2}\cdot{}^i\delta x_2\right]$$

$$= \frac{1}{N}\left(\frac{\partial y_1}{\partial x_1}\cdot\frac{\partial y_2}{\partial x_1}\right)\sum_{i=1}^{N}({}^i\delta x_1)^2$$

$$+ \frac{1}{N}\left(\frac{\partial y_1}{\partial x_2}\cdot\frac{\partial y_2}{\partial x_2}\right)\sum_{i=1}^{N}({}^i\delta x_2)^2$$

$$+ \frac{2}{N}\left(\frac{\partial y_1}{\partial x_1}\cdot\frac{\partial y_2}{\partial x_2} + \frac{\partial y_1}{\partial x_2}\cdot\frac{\partial y_2}{\partial x_1}\right)\sum_{i=1}^{N}({}^i\delta x_1)({}^i\delta x_2)$$

Again the last term is proportional to $\text{cov}(x_1, x_2)$ and is therefore zero and the first two terms are proportional to $\text{var}(x_1)$ and $\text{var}(x_2)$ respectively. Hence:

$$\text{cov}(y_1, y_2) = \left(\frac{\partial y_1}{\partial x_1} \cdot \frac{\partial y_2}{\partial x_1}\right) \text{var}(x_1) + \left(\frac{\partial y_1}{\partial x_2} \cdot \frac{\partial y_2}{\partial x_2}\right) \text{var}(x_2) \quad (2.2\text{-}3)$$

For practical purposes, these equations are expressed in terms of the standard deviations and correlation coefficient. Conversion of the formulae is trivial and they are shown below for reference:

Propagation of the standard deviations of two uncorrelated observables to the standard deviations and correlation coefficient of two parameters using the derivatives $(\partial y_i / \partial x_j)$

$$\sigma(y_1) = \left[\left(\frac{\partial y_1}{\partial x_1}\right)^2 \sigma^2(x_1) + \left(\frac{\partial y_1}{\partial x_2}\right)^2 \sigma^2(x_2)\right]^{\frac{1}{2}}$$

$$\sigma(y_2) = \left[\left(\frac{\partial y_2}{\partial x_1}\right)^2 \sigma^2(x_1) + \left(\frac{\partial y_2}{\partial x_2}\right)^2 \sigma^2(x_2)\right]^{\frac{1}{2}}$$

$$\rho(y_1, y_2) = \frac{1}{\sigma(y_1)\sigma(y_2)} \times \left[\left(\frac{\partial y_1}{\partial x_1} \cdot \frac{\partial y_2}{\partial x_1}\right) \sigma^2(x_1)\right.$$

$$\left. + \left(\frac{\partial y_1}{\partial x_2} \cdot \frac{\partial y_2}{\partial x_2}\right) \sigma^2(x_2)\right] \quad (2.2\text{-}4)$$

The formulae above use the derivatives $(\partial y_i / \partial x_j)$ which, as mentioned earlier, may not be available. Equations (2.1-5) can be used to convert these formulae so that the other set of derivatives is used. The resulting equations are shown below:

Continued on next page

Propagation of the standard deviations of two uncorrelated observables to the standard deviations and correlation coefficient of two parameters using the derivatives $(\partial x_i / \partial y_j)$

$$\sigma(y_1) = \left[\left(\frac{\partial x_2}{\partial y_2} \right)^2 \sigma^2(x_1) + \left(\frac{\partial x_1}{\partial y_2} \right)^2 \sigma^2(x_2) \right]^{\frac{1}{2}} \Big/ |J|$$

$$\sigma(y_2) = \left[\left(\frac{\partial x_2}{\partial y_1} \right)^2 \sigma^2(x_1) + \left(\frac{\partial x_1}{\partial y_1} \right)^2 \sigma^2(x_2) \right]^{\frac{1}{2}} \Big/ |J|$$

$$\rho(y_1, y_2) = -\frac{1}{J^2 \sigma(y_1) \sigma(y_2)} \times \left[\left(\frac{\partial x_2}{\partial y_2} \cdot \frac{\partial x_2}{\partial y_1} \right) \sigma^2(x_1) \right.$$

$$\left. + \left(\frac{\partial x_1}{\partial y_1} \cdot \frac{\partial x_1}{\partial y_2} \right) \sigma^2(x_2) \right]$$

where

$$J = \begin{vmatrix} \dfrac{\partial x_1}{\partial y_1} & \dfrac{\partial x_1}{\partial y_2} \\[2ex] \dfrac{\partial x_2}{\partial y_1} & \dfrac{\partial x_2}{\partial y_2} \end{vmatrix} \qquad (2.2.5)$$

and $|J|$ is the absolute (positive) value of J.

Finally there are two particularly convenient methods for calculating the correlation coefficient, which can be used if its sign is known in advance, and which can result in considerable saving of time in repetitive calculations. Often the sign of ρ can be inferred from the form of the relationship between y_1, y_2 and x_1, x_2, or experience in previous calculations allows it to be predicted.

The necessary equations are derived by considering the quantity

$$\text{var}(y_1)\,\text{var}(y_2) - [\text{cov}(y_1, y_2)]^2$$

If eqns. (2.2-1), (2.2-2) and (2.2-3) are used to substitute for $\text{var}(y_1)$, $\text{var}(y_2)$ and $\text{cov}(y_1, y_2)$ in this quantity, after some manipulation the following equation is obtained:

$$\text{var}(y_1)\,\text{var}(y_2) - [\text{cov}(y_1, y_2)]^2 = J^2\,\text{var}(x_1)\,\text{var}(x_2) \qquad (2.2\text{-}6)$$

Here J is the Jacobian determinant given by eqn. (2.1-6).

J is also given by:

$$J = \begin{vmatrix} \dfrac{\partial y_1}{\partial x_1} & \dfrac{\partial y_1}{\partial x_2} \\[2ex] \dfrac{\partial y_2}{\partial x_1} & \dfrac{\partial y_2}{\partial x_2} \end{vmatrix}^{-1} \qquad (2.2\text{-}7)$$

Thus either set of derivatives can be used to calculate $[\mathrm{cov}(y_1, y_2)]^2$ using eqn. (2.2-6). The formulae are shown below in terms of the correlation coefficient:

Obtaining the correlation coefficient when the sign is known, if the two observables are uncorrelated

---

$$\rho(y_1, y_2) = \pm\left[1 - \frac{J^2 \sigma^2(x_1)\sigma^2(x_2)}{\sigma^2(y_1)\sigma^2(y_2)}\right]^{\frac{1}{2}}$$

where

$$J = \begin{vmatrix} \dfrac{\partial x_1}{\partial y_1} & \dfrac{\partial x_1}{\partial y_1} \\[2ex] \dfrac{\partial x_2}{\partial y_1} & \dfrac{\partial x_2}{\partial y_2} \end{vmatrix}$$

$$= \begin{vmatrix} \dfrac{\partial y_1}{\partial x_1} & \dfrac{\partial y_1}{\partial x_2} \\[2ex] \dfrac{\partial y_2}{\partial x_1} & \dfrac{\partial y_2}{\partial x_2} \end{vmatrix}^{-1} \qquad (2.2\text{-}8)$$

2.3 THE ERROR ELLIPSE

In Chapter 1 the correlation coefficient was described as a measure of the extent to which errors in two quantities are correlated. It is therefore directly related to the probability of particular *pairs* of values occurring. This can be seen by example in Section 1.6 and Fig. 1.2. In this section, the relationship between the correlation coefficient and the probability distribution of two quantities will be given a geometrical interpretation in terms of the *error ellipse*. Strictly speaking, this interpretation applies only to quantities that have a certain type of distribution, of which the normal or Gaussian distribution is an example. However, as many experimental cases have approximately normal distributions, the interpretation has fairly general significance. Moreover, it applies not only to problems in which there are two observables or parameters, but also to each pair of quantities in a multivariate problem.

For a normal distribution, the probability of an observable having a value between x_1 and $x_1 + dx_1$ is given by

$$P(x_1)\,dx_1 = k_1 \exp\left(-\frac{(\delta x_1)^2}{2\sigma^2(x_1)}\right) dx_1 \qquad (2.3\text{-}1)$$

where k_1 is a constant. Similarly for x_2

$$P(x_2)\,dx_2 = k_2 \exp\left(-\frac{(\delta x_2)^2}{2\sigma^2(x_2)}\right) dx_2 \qquad (2.3\text{-}2)$$

If x_1 and x_2 are measured independently, then the probability of having the pair of values $x_1 \to x_1 + dx_1$, $x_2 \to x_2 + dx_2$ is given simply by the product of these two probabilities:

$$P(x_1, x_2)\,dx_1\,dx_2 = k_1 k_2 \exp\left[-\frac{(\delta x_1)^2}{2\sigma^2(x_1)} - \frac{(\delta x_2)^2}{2\sigma^2(x_2)}\right] dx_1\,dx_2 \qquad (2.3\text{-}3)$$

The ellipse:

$$\frac{(\delta x_1)^2}{\sigma^2(x_1)} + \frac{(\delta x_2)^2}{\sigma^2(x_2)} = 1 \qquad (2.3\text{-}4)$$

is plotted in Fig. 2.1. The curve represents pairs of values of x_1 and x_2 that have a probability of $e^{-\frac{1}{2}}$ times the maximum probability. All points inside the ellipse have a greater probability than this and all points outside a smaller probability. The ellipse is therefore a probability contour giving some indication of the distribution of pairs of values and is called the *error ellipse*. The axes of the ellipse are seen to coincide with the graph axes; an indication, as we shall see later, that the covariance and correlation coefficient are zero.

Figure 2.1 illustrates the error ellipse for the two observables. We now wish to display the error ellipse for the two parameters, y_1 and y_2, whose errors are correlated. If observables in the range $x_1 \to x_1 + dx_1$, $x_2 \to x_2 + dx_2$ give parameters in the range $y_1 \to y_1 + dy_1$, $y_2 \to y_2 + dy_2$, then the probability of obtaining parameters in the latter range will be given by

$$P(y_1, y_2)\,dy_1\,dy_2 = P(x_1, x_2)\,dx_1\,dx_2$$

$$= k_1 k_2 \exp -\left[\frac{(\delta x_1)^2}{2\sigma^2(x_1)} - \frac{(\delta x_2)^2}{2\sigma^2(x_2)}\right] dx_1\,dx_2$$

$$(2.3\text{-}5)$$

If δy_1 and δy_2 are substituted for δx_1 and δx_2 using eqns. (2.1-3) and $\sigma(y_1)$, $\sigma(y_2)$ and $\rho(y_1, y_2)$ substituted for $\sigma(x_1)$ and $\sigma(x_2)$ using eqns. (2.2-5), it can be shown after much manipulation that

$$P(y_1, y_2)$$
$$= k_1 k_2 \exp\left[-\frac{1}{2(1-\rho^2)}\left\{\frac{(\delta y_1)^2}{\sigma_2(y_1)} + \frac{(\delta y_2)^2}{\sigma^2(y_2)} - \frac{2\rho\,\delta y_1\,\delta y_2}{\sigma(y_1)\sigma(y_2)}\right\}\right]$$

$$(2.3\text{-}6)$$

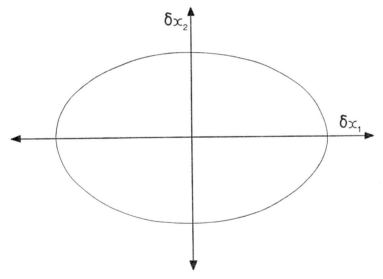

FIG. 2.1   Error ellipse for two uncorrelated quantities.

The error ellipse for y_1 and y_2 is therefore

$$\frac{(\delta y_1)^2}{\sigma^2(y_1)} + \frac{(\delta y_2)^2}{\sigma^2(y_2)} - \frac{2\rho(y_1, y_2)\delta y_1\,\delta y_2}{\sigma(y_1)\sigma(y_2)} = 1 - \rho^2(y_1, y_2) \quad (2.3\text{-}7)$$

and this is shown in Fig. 2.2. The axes of the ellipse can be seen to no longer coincide with the axes of the graph. The tilting of the ellipse means that the probability of finding a particular value of y_1 very much depends on the value of y_2. The figure illustrates how probabilities must be considered in pairs. It is instructive to compare this type of diagram with the actual values in a specific case as shown in Fig. 1.2.

Figure 2.2 shows an error ellipse for a positive correlation co-efficient that for a negative correlation coefficient would tilt the other way. The extent of the elongation of the ellipse depends on the

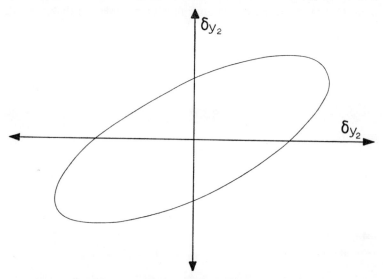

FIG. 2.2   Error ellipse for two correlated quantities.

value of ρ. Figure 2.3 shows error ellipses for equal and constant values of $\sigma(y_1)$ and $\sigma(y_2)$ but varying values of $\rho(y_1, y_2)$. As can be seen the correlation of errors does not become significant below $\rho = 0.5$ and it is not until $\rho = 0.9$ that the error ellipse becomes greatly distorted. As $\rho \to \pm 1$ the ellipse becomes a straight line of finite length. This is the case with the overlapping peaks discussed in Section 1.5.

In considering the results of a multivariate error analysis, it is usually sufficient therefore to confine one's attention to cases where the correlation coefficient is greater than 0·9. In some cases it will not be possible to do more than take note of the high value of ρ in con-sidering the significance of the results. In other cases it will be possible to redesign the experiment to reduce the value of ρ. A high value of ρ indicates that the parameters are not well determined by the observables. Changing the conditions under which the observables are measured might make it possible to improve the situation. The

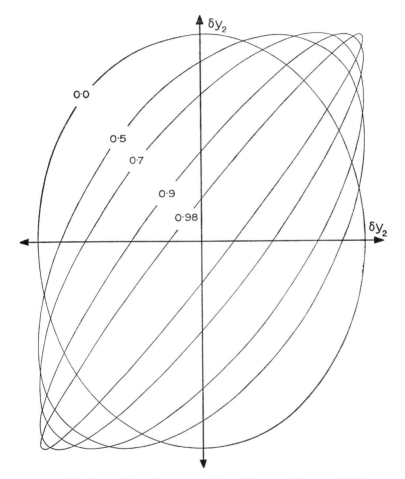

FIG. 2.3 Error ellipses for various values of the correlation coefficient.

approach used depends on the particular experiment and this problem will be discussed in some of the later examples. Redesign of an experiment to reduce the correlation coefficient will often also result in an improvement in the standard deviations.

2.4 THE CONDITIONAL STANDARD DEVIATION

For two uncorrelated quantities, the maximum values of the differences on the error ellipse are equal to the standard deviations; e.g. the maximum value of δx_1 in Fig. 2.1 is $\sigma(x_1)$. These maximum values occur on the graph axes. For correlated quantities, it can be shown using eqn. (2.3-7), that the maximum values of the differences are still equal to standard deviations, although they no longer occur on the axes; e.g. the maximum value of δy_1 in Fig. 2.2 is $\sigma(y_1)$ as indicated. The values of the intercepts are now less than the standard deviations and the term *conditional standard deviation* is used to describe their positive values. For example, the intercept on the positive δy_1 axis is the conditional standard deviation of y_1 and is given the symbol $\sigma(y_1, y_2 = \bar{y}_2)$. It is the standard deviation of y_1 if y_2 were known by some other method to have the value $\bar{y}_2$.

From eqn. (2.3-7) it can be shown readily that

$$\sigma(y_1, y_2 = \bar{y}_2) = \sigma(y_1)[1 - \rho^2(y_1, y_2)]^{\frac{1}{2}} \qquad (2.4\text{-}1)$$

and that

$$\sigma(y_2, y_1 = \bar{y}_1) = \sigma(y_2)[1 - \rho^2(y_1, y_2)]^{\frac{1}{2}} \qquad (2.4\text{-}2)$$

TABLE 2.1

THE CORRELATION COEFFICIENT AND THE CONDITIONAL STANDARD DEVIATION

Correlation coefficient	Conditional standard deviation / Standard deviation
0	1·00
0·10	0·995
0·15	0·99
0·20	0·98
0·30	0·95
0·40	0·92
0·50	9·87
0·60	0·80
0·70	0·71
0·80	0·60
0·85	0·53
0·90	0·43
0·95	0·31
0·98	0·20
0·99	0·14
0·995	0·10
1·00	0

Thus the higher the value of ρ the smaller the conditional standard deviation in comparison to the ordinary standard deviation. For reference purposes, rough values of the ratio of these quantities for various values of ρ are given in Table 2.1.

The conditional standard deviations are an alternative to the correlation coefficient as a way of describing the error situation of two quantities. Their significance can be visualised more directly, but they have the disadvantage that four rather than three parameters are involved altogether, and also they assume something about the distribution function. For a multivariate problem, each parameter has a conditional standard deviation with respect to every other parameter.

2.5 UNCORRELATED OBSERVABLES: AN EXAMPLE

The example chosen here is the calculation of the internuclear distances in the hydrogen cyanide, HCN, molecule. The molecule is known to be linear and the bond distances are given the symbols r_1 and r_2 as shown below:

The molecule deuterium cyanide, DCN, in which the hydrogen has been replaced by its isotope deuterium, is believed to have an identical structure with identical internuclear distances:

The moments of inertia of the two molecules will be different, however, as hydrogen and deuterium have different masses. The moments of inertia of both molecules have been measured using microwave spectroscopy and these values can be used to obtain values for r_1 and r_2.

If I_1 and I_2 are the moments of inertia of HCN and DCN respectively, then the equations relating them to r_1 and r_2 are as follows:

$$I_1 = (1{\cdot}610\,909r_1{}^2 + 11{\cdot}196\,706r_2{}^2 + 1{\cdot}735\,001r_1r_2) \times 10^{-27}$$

$$I_2 = (3{\cdot}103\,716r_1{}^2 + 11{\cdot}629\,620r_2{}^2 + 3{\cdot}342\,802r_1r_2) \times 10^{-27}$$

Experimental values for I_1 and I_2 have been obtained to be:

$$I_1 = 1 \cdot 8850 \times 10^{-46} \text{ kg m}^2$$

$$I_2 = 2 \cdot 3098 \times 10^{-46} \text{ kg m}^2$$

From these the internuclear distances are calculated using the relationships given above:

$$r_1 = 1 \cdot 0657 \times 10^{-10} \text{ m}$$

$$r_2 = 1 \cdot 1530 \times 10^{-10} \text{ m}$$

We are now concerned to calculate the errors in these bond distances. Estimates of the standard deviations of the observables, made from a knowledge of the apparatus are

$$\sigma(I_1) = 4 \times 10^{-50} \text{ kg m}^2$$

and

$$\sigma(I_2) = 6 \times 10^{-50} \text{ kg m}^2$$

These measurements were made independently and are therefore assumed to be uncorrelated. Inversion of the relationship between the moments of inertia and the bond lengths is not straightforward and hence the derivatives $(\partial x_i / \partial y_j) \equiv (\partial I_i / \partial r_j)$ are used for the propagation. These are calculated to be as follows:

$$\frac{\partial I_1}{\partial r_1} = (2 \times 1 \cdot 610\,909 r_1 + 1 \cdot 735\,001 r_2) \times 10^{-27}$$

$$= 5 \cdot 433\,948 \times 10^{-37}$$

$$\frac{\partial I_1}{\partial r_2} = (1 \cdot 735\,001 r_1 + 2 \times 11 \cdot 196\,706 r_2) \times 10^{-27}$$

$$= 27 \cdot 668\,595 \times 10^{-37}$$

$$\frac{\partial I_2}{\partial r_1} = (2 \times 3 \cdot 103\,716 r_1 + 3 \cdot 342\,802 r_2) \times 10^{-27}$$

$$= 10 \cdot 469\,511 \times 10^{-37}$$

$$\frac{\partial I_2}{\partial r_2} = (3 \cdot 342\,802 r_1 + 2 \times 11 \cdot 629\,620 r_2) \times 10^{-27}$$

$$= 30 \cdot 380\,328 \times 10^{-37}$$

The Jacobian determinant is also calculated to be

$$J = \begin{vmatrix} 5 \cdot 433\,948 & 27 \cdot 668\,595 \\ 10 \cdot 469\,511 & 30 \cdot 380\,328 \end{vmatrix} \times 10^{-74} = -124 \cdot 592 \times 10^{-74}$$

The standard deviations and the correlation coefficient for the two internuclear distances can now be obtained using eqns. (2.2-5)

$$\sigma(r_1) = 1 \cdot 1 \times 10^{-13} \, \text{m}$$

$$\sigma(r_2) = 0 \cdot 9 \times 10^{-13} \, \text{m}$$

$$\rho(r_1, r_2) = -0 \cdot 98$$

The results can therefore be quoted as

$$r_1 = 1 \cdot 0657 \pm 0 \cdot 0011 \times 10^{-10} \, \text{m}$$

and

$$r_2 = 1 \cdot 1530 \pm 0 \cdot 0009 \times 10^{-10} \, \text{m}$$

Although the errors in the moments of inertia are about 0·02 per cent, the errors in the bond distances are about 0·1 per cent. This is in spite of the fact that the moments of inertia depend on the bond lengths to the second power and one might therefore expect a smaller error in these parameters. In fact the parameter errors are about ten times greater than one might hope for under favourable circumstances. The reason for this can be seen in the high correlation coefficient of $-0 \cdot 98$, indicating that the parameters are poorly determined by the observables in this case. The error ellipse for $\rho = 0 \cdot 98$ is shown in Fig. 2.3 and indicates the sort of distribution we might expect in this case for pairs of values.

To improve the errors and reduce the correlation coefficient further observables are needed such as moments of inertia of other isotopically substituted molecules or else diffraction data. Such experiments and calculations have in fact been done.

2.6 TWO CORRELATED OBSERVABLES

We now no longer assume that the observables are measured independently and thus the error propagation now starts from the standard deviations plus the correlation coefficient of the two observables. In Section 2.2 it was shown that the variance of one of the parameters is given by

$$\text{var}(y_1) = \frac{1}{N} \left(\frac{\partial y_1}{\partial x_1} \right)^2 \sum_{i=1}^{N} ({}^i \delta x_1)^2 + \frac{1}{N} \left(\frac{\partial y_1}{\partial x_2} \right)^2 \sum_{i=1}^{N} ({}^i \delta x_2)^2$$

$$+ \frac{2}{N} \left(\frac{\partial y_1}{\partial x_1} \cdot \frac{\partial y_1}{\partial x_2} \right) \sum_{i=1}^{N} ({}^i \delta x_1)({}^i \delta x_2)$$

The last term, which was previously neglected, must now be included since it is proportional to $\text{cov}(x_1, x_2)$. Thus:

$$\text{var}(y_1) = \left(\frac{\partial y_1}{\partial x_1}\right)^2 \text{var}(x_1) + \left(\frac{\partial y_1}{\partial x_2}\right)^2 \text{var}(x_2)$$

$$+ 2\left(\frac{\partial y_1}{\partial x_1} \cdot \frac{\partial y_1}{\partial x_2}\right) \text{cov}(x_1, x_2) \qquad (2.6\text{-}1)$$

And also:

$$\text{var}(y_2) = \left(\frac{\partial y_2}{\partial x_1}\right)^2 \text{var}(x_1) + \left(\frac{\partial y_2}{\partial x_2}\right)^2 \text{var}(x_2)$$

$$+ 2\left(\frac{\partial y_2}{\partial x_1} \cdot \frac{\partial y_2}{\partial x_1}\right) \text{cov}(x_1, x_2) \qquad (2.6\text{-}2)$$

Similarly the corresponding expression for $\text{cov}(y_1, y_2)$ has been shown in Section 2.2 to be

$$\text{cov}(y_1, y_2) = \frac{1}{N}\left(\frac{\partial y_1}{\partial x_1} \cdot \frac{\partial y_2}{\partial x_1}\right) \sum_{i=1}^{N} (^i\delta x_1)^2$$

$$+ \frac{1}{N}\left(\frac{\partial y_1}{\partial x_2} \cdot \frac{\partial y_1}{\partial x_2}\right) \sum_{i=1}^{N} (^i\delta x_2)^2$$

$$+ \frac{1}{N}\left(\frac{\partial y_1}{\partial x_1} \cdot \frac{\partial y_2}{\partial x_2} + \frac{\partial y_1}{\partial x_2} \cdot \frac{\partial y_2}{\partial x_1}\right) \sum_{i=1}^{N} (^i\delta x_1)(^i\delta x_2)$$

And therefore

$$\text{cov}(y_1, y_2) = \left(\frac{\partial y_1}{\partial x_1} \cdot \frac{\partial y_2}{\partial x_1}\right) \text{var}(x_1) + \left(\frac{\partial y_1}{\partial x_2} \cdot \frac{\partial y_2}{\partial x_2}\right) \text{var}(x_2)$$

$$+ \left(\frac{\partial y_1}{\partial x_1} \cdot \frac{\partial y_2}{\partial x_2} + \frac{\partial y_1}{\partial x_2} \cdot \frac{\partial y_2}{\partial x_1}\right) \text{cov}(x_1, x_2) \qquad (2.6\text{-}3)$$

These equations are summarised below in terms of the standard deviations and correlation coefficient:

Propagation of the standard deviations and correlation coefficient of two observables to the standard deviations and correlation coefficient of two parameters, using the derivatives $(\partial y_i/\partial x_j)$

$$\sigma(y_1) = \left[\left(\frac{\partial y_1}{\partial x_1}\right)^2 \sigma^2(x_1) + \left(\frac{\partial y_1}{\partial x_2}\right)^2 \sigma^2(x_2)\right.$$

$$\left. + 2\left(\frac{\partial y_1}{\partial x_1}\cdot\frac{\partial y_1}{\partial x_2}\right)\sigma(x_1)\sigma(x_2)\rho(x_1,x_2)\right]^{\frac{1}{2}}$$

$$\sigma(y_2) = \left[\left(\frac{\partial y_2}{\partial x_1}\right)^2 \sigma^2(x_1) + \left(\frac{\partial y_2}{\partial x_2}\right)^2 \sigma^2(x_2)\right.$$

$$\left. + 2\left(\frac{\partial y_2}{\partial x_1}\cdot\frac{\partial y_2}{\partial x_2}\right)\sigma(x_1)\sigma(x_2)\rho(x_1,x_2)\right]^{\frac{1}{2}}$$

$$\rho(y_1,y_2) = \frac{1}{\sigma(y_1)\sigma(y_2)}\left[\left(\frac{\partial y_1}{\partial x_1}\cdot\frac{\partial y_2}{\partial x_1}\right)\sigma^2(x_1)\right.$$

$$+ \left(\frac{\partial y_1}{\partial x_2}\cdot\frac{\partial y_2}{\partial x_2}\right)\sigma^2(x_2)$$

$$+ \left(\frac{\partial y_1}{\partial x_1}\cdot\frac{\partial y_2}{\partial x_2} + \frac{\partial y_1}{\partial x_2}\cdot\frac{\partial y_2}{\partial x_1}\right)$$

$$\left.\times\ \sigma(x_1)\sigma(x_2)\rho(x_1,x_2)\right] \qquad (2.6\text{-}4)$$

There will also be a set of equations using the $(\partial x_i/\partial y_j)$ which will be used when the other set is not readily available.

Continued on next page

Propagation of the standard deviations and correlation coefficient of two observables to the standard deviations and correlation coefficient of two parameters, using the derivatives $(\partial x_i/\partial y_j)$

$$\sigma(y_1) = \left[\left(\frac{\partial x_2}{\partial y_2}\right)^2 \sigma^2(x_1) + \left(\frac{\partial x_1}{\partial y_2}\right)^2 \sigma^2(x_2)\right.$$

$$\left. - 2\left(\frac{\partial x_1}{\partial y_2} \cdot \frac{\partial x_2}{\partial y_2}\right)\sigma(x_1)\sigma(x_2)\rho(x_1, x_2)\right]^{\frac{1}{2}}\bigg/|J|$$

$$\sigma(y_2) = \left[\left(\frac{\partial x_2}{\partial y_1}\right)^2 \sigma^2(x_1) + \left(\frac{\partial x_1}{\partial y_1}\right)^2 \sigma^2(x_2)\right.$$

$$\left. - 2\left(\frac{\partial x_1}{\partial y_1} \cdot \frac{\partial x_2}{\partial y_1}\right)\sigma(x_1)\sigma(x_2)\rho(x_1, x_2)\right]^{\frac{1}{2}}\bigg/|J|$$

$$\rho(y_1, y_2) = -\frac{1}{J^2\sigma(y_1)\sigma(y_2)}\left[\left(\frac{\partial x_2}{\partial y_1} \cdot \frac{\partial x_2}{\partial y_2}\right)\sigma^2(x_1)\right.$$

$$+ \left(\frac{\partial x_1}{\partial y_1} \cdot \frac{\partial x_1}{\partial y_2}\right)\sigma^2(x_2)$$

$$- \left(\frac{\partial x_1}{\partial y_1} \cdot \frac{\partial x_2}{\partial y_2} + \frac{\partial x_1}{\partial y_2} \cdot \frac{\partial x_2}{\partial y_1}\right)$$

$$\left. \times \sigma(x_1)\sigma(x_2)\rho(x_1, x_2)\right]$$

where

$$J = \begin{vmatrix} \dfrac{\partial x_1}{\partial y_1} & \dfrac{\partial x_1}{\partial y_2} \\[2mm] \dfrac{\partial x_2}{\partial y_1} & \dfrac{\partial x_2}{\partial y_2} \end{vmatrix}$$

(2.6-5)

and $|J|$ is the absolute (positive) value of J.

Finally there is a convenient method for calculating the parameter correlation coefficient from either set of derivatives, when the sign is known in advance. The arguments are analogous to those in Section 2.2 for uncorrelated observables. The basic equation is found to be:

$$\text{var}(y_1)\,\text{var}(y_2) - [\text{cov}(y_1, y_2)]^2$$
$$= J^2\{\text{var}(x_1)\,\text{var}(x_2) - [\text{cov}(x_1, x_2)]^2\} \qquad (2.6\text{-}6)$$

In terms of the standard deviations and correlation coefficients, the formulae are as follows:

Obtaining the correlation coefficient when the sign is known, if the two observables are correlated

$$\rho(y_1, y_2) = \pm\left[1 - \frac{J^2\sigma^2(x_1)\sigma^2(x_2)[1 - \rho^2(x_1, x_2)]}{\sigma^2(y_1)\sigma^2(y_2)}\right]^{\frac{1}{2}}$$

where

$$J = \begin{vmatrix} \dfrac{\partial x_1}{\partial y_1} & \dfrac{\partial x_1}{\partial y_2} \\[2ex] \dfrac{\partial x_2}{\partial y_1} & \dfrac{\partial x_2}{\partial y_2} \end{vmatrix}$$

$$= \begin{vmatrix} \dfrac{\delta y_1}{\partial x_1} & \dfrac{\partial y_1}{\partial x_2} \\[2ex] \dfrac{\partial y_2}{\partial x_1} & \dfrac{\partial y_2}{\partial x_2} \end{vmatrix}^{-1} \qquad (2.6\text{-}7)$$

The procedure in using the above equations is a straightforward extension of that for uncorrelated observables and so no example will be given. The equations may also be used to propagate errors from two parameters to two further parameters, as discussed in the introductory chapter.

2.7 ERRORS IN MANY PREDICTED OBSERVABLES OBTAINED FROM TWO PARAMETERS

Sometimes it will be required to predict the values of several observables from two parameters and to give estimates of errors in these predicted values. The predicted observables, $x_1, x_2, x_3, \ldots$ etc. will not be independent quantities and the derivatives $(\partial x_i/\partial y_j)$ must be used. Usually, we will not be interested in obtaining values of the correlation coefficients, $\rho(x_i, x_j)$, for the predicted observables, but it is important to include the correlation coefficient for the parameters, $\rho(y_1, y_2)$, in the calculation. The theory of the error propagation is identical to that given in Section 2.6, and the equation for $\sigma(x_i)$ is therefore as follows:

Calculation of the standard deviation of a predicted observable

$$\sigma(x_i) = \left[\left(\frac{\partial x_i}{\partial y_1}\right)^2 \sigma^2(y_1) + \left(\frac{\partial x_i}{\partial y_2}\right)^2 \sigma^2(y_2) \right.$$

$$\left. + 2 \left(\frac{\partial x_i}{\partial y_1} \cdot \frac{\partial x_i}{\partial y_2}\right) \sigma(y_1)\sigma(y_2)\rho(y_1, y_2) \right]^{\frac{1}{2}} \qquad (2.7\text{-}1)$$

As an example of this procedure, we will calculate the errors in the rate constants, k_i, for chemical reactions predicted for various temperatures, T_i, by the Arrhenius equation

$$k_i = A \exp\left(\frac{-E}{8\cdot314 T_i}\right) \qquad (2.7\text{-}2)$$

A and E are the two Arrhenius parameters, which in the example given have the values:

$$A = 1\cdot26 \times 10^8 \text{ s}^{-1}$$

and

$$E = 4\cdot784 \times 10^4 \text{ J mole}^{-1}$$

The standard deviations and the correlation coefficients are known to be:

$$\sigma(A) = 3\cdot9 \times 10^7$$

$$\sigma(E) = 7\cdot9 \times 10^2$$

and

$$\rho(A, E) = 0\cdot9971$$

The derivatives which need to be calculated are as follows:

$$\frac{\partial k_i}{\partial A} = \exp\left(\frac{-E}{8\cdot314 T_i}\right)$$

$$\frac{\partial k_i}{\partial E} = -\left(\frac{A}{8\cdot314 T_i}\right) \exp\left(\frac{-E}{8\cdot314 T_i}\right) \qquad (2.7\text{-}3)$$

At $T = 300$ K the following values are obtained.

$$k_i = 0.5897$$

$$\frac{\partial k_i}{\partial A} = 4.679\ 85 \times 10^{-9}$$

$$\frac{\partial k_i}{\partial E} = -2.364\ 13 \times 10^{-4}$$

$\sigma(k_i)$ can now be calculated using eqn. (2.7-1)

$$\sigma(k_i) = (0.032\ 769\ 7 + 0.035\ 200\ 6 - 0.067\ 729\ 6)^{\frac{1}{2}}$$
$$= 0.0158$$

The first two terms in this equation are almost cancelled by the final term, which involves the correlation coefficient. In fact the result for $\sigma(k_i)$ is about sixteen times less than it would have been if the correlation coefficient had been ignored.

Values of k_i and $\sigma(k_i)$ have been calculated for a range of values of T_i and are tabulated in Table 2.2. It is interesting to see how the

TABLE 2.2

ERRORS IN PREDICTED RATE CONSTANTS

T_i	k_i	$\sigma(k_i)$	Percentage Error
100	1.291×10^{-17}	7.09×10^{-18}	54
150	2.760×10^{-9}	9.14×10^{-10}	33
200	4.034×10^{-5}	6.97×10^{-6}	17
250	1.272×10^{-2}	1.01×10^{-3}	7
300	$0.589\ 7$	$0.015\ 8$	3
350	9.132	0.372	4
400	71.29	5.09	7
450	3.525×10^2	34.15	10
500	1.266×10^3	148.8	11

rough values for the percentage error in the rate constant, given in the final column, vary over the temperature range. They reach a minimum in the $T_i = 300$–350 region. This is because the Arrhenius parameters were originally obtained from measurements made in this temperature range. (The calculation in which they were obtained will be given in Chapter 3.) This example therefore demonstrates how well information about the reliability of the data is carried by the correlation coefficient in conjunction with the standard deviations.

2.8 PROPAGATION OF ERRORS TO NON-INDEPENDENT PARAMETERS

The procedures relevant here have been alluded to before and need only to be briefly summarised. As the parameters are not independent, the derivatives $(\partial y_i / \partial x_j)$ must be used. Apart from this consideration, we can treat every pair of new parameters as an independent set. Thus equations of the form of (2.6-4) for every pair of new parameters are appropriate.

CHAPTER 3

Errors in two parameters obtained from several observables

3.1 INTRODUCTION

In this chapter we show how to obtain the standard deviations, $\sigma(y_1)$ and $\sigma(y_2)$ and the correlation coefficient $\rho(y_1, y_2)$ of the parameters y_1 and y_2, which have been obtained from the n observables $x_1, x_2, \ldots, x_n$. The observables are assumed throughout the chapter to be uncorrelated, *i.e.* measured independently. The methods of Chapter 5 must be used for correlated observables. It is also assumed that the derivatives, $\partial x_i / \partial y_j$ have negligible errors. If not, this problem is also dealt with in Section 5.8.

In any calculation the parameters themselves will first have to be obtained. These can be calculated from any pair of observables and are therefore overdetermined. It can be shown that the best estimates of y_1 and y_2, *i.e.* the estimates with the minimum variance, are obtained using the *principle of least-squares*; that is, adjusting the values of y_1 and y_2 until the sum of the squares of the differences between the observed values of the x_i and the values calculated from y_1 and y_2 is at a minimum.

The principle of least-squares leads to the linear least-squares equations for a linear problem and to the method of least-squares refinement for a non-linear problem. The appropriate equations are given in Section 3.4, but as discussed in the introduction to the first chapter, least-squares methods may not be the best way of finding the parameters in a particular problem and other more technical methods, still using the principle of least-squares, can be used.

3.2 PROPAGATION VERSUS CALCULATION

When the parameters are overdetermined, there are two methods of obtaining their standard deviations: either by *propagation* from the errors in the observables as in the last chapter, or by *calculation* from the sum of the squares of the differences (the quantity which is minimised in the least-squares treatment). The scientist will need to choose between the two methods in his particular case.

The precision to which the standard deviations are estimated by the second method depends on the difference between the number of observables and parameters, in this case $n - 2$. As before, if $n - 2$ is six then for common distributions the standard deviation will be estimated to around 10 per cent; a very acceptable state of affairs. Thus if $n - 2$ is six or greater, then calculation is likely to be better than propagation and vice versa. An exception to this rule is when it is felt that there are consistent errors which do not show up in the scatter of observables. Then the standard deviations of the observables should be adjusted upwards, as indicated in Section 1.3 and the errors propagated.

3.3 WEIGHTING

So far it has been tacitly assumed that the errors in all the observables are equal. In general this will not be so and in this case the principle of least-squares states that it is the *weighted* sum of the squares of the differences that must be minimised to obtain the best estimates of the parameters. The appropriate weighting method is to divide each element in the sum by a number proportional to the variance of the observable from which it was calculated. Let w_{ii} be the weight corresponding to the observable x_i, then

$$w_{ii} = \frac{\sigma^2}{\sigma^2(x_i)} \tag{3.3-1}$$

where σ^2 is a constant: the variance of an observable of unit weight. The sum to be minimised in the least-squares calculation is then

$$S = \sum_{i=1}^{n} \varepsilon^2(x_i) w_{ii} \tag{3.3-2}$$

where

$$\varepsilon(x_i) = x_i(\text{observed}) - x_i(\text{calculated}) \tag{3.3-3}$$

Weighting therefore modifies all the least-squares equations, as will be seen in the next section, and is also taken into account, of course, when the principle of least-squares is used with other parameter-fitting methods.

Weighting is also involved in the error analysis. For correct and consistent results, the same weighting must be used in the parameter-fitting and the error-analysis calculations.

In the case of an error *propagation*, the weights used will be simply the inverses of the variances, *i.e.* $\sigma^2 = 1$ in eqn. (3.3-1). In an error *calculation*, the variances are not known in advance. Nevertheless, values for the weights must be decided on. In other words, although the absolute values of the variances of the observables need not be known for parameter-fitting and error-calculation, effectively the relative values must be assigned.

3.4 LEAST-SQUARES EQUATIONS AND REFINEMENT

The equations in this section will be stated but not proved. Their derivation is set out in several textbooks and is given in Chapter 5 for the general case of several parameters. In outline, the procedure used for this is to differentiate an expression for the weighted sum of the squares of the differences with respect to each parameter and set the results equal to zero. This gives two simultaneous equations, which can be solved for the two parameters.

All the equations given here will be for weighted least-squares. The unweighted equations are readily obtained by setting all the w_{ii} equal to unity.

The linear equations are first given. These are for situations where

$$x_i = a_{i1}y_1 + a_{i2}y_2 \tag{3.4-1}$$

for all i, the a_{ij} being constants. The situation where

$$x_i = a_{i0} + a_{i1}y_1 + a_{i2}y_2 \tag{3.4-2}$$

can easily be accommodated by using $x_i - a_{i0}$ as the observable. The best estimates of y_1 and y_2 are then given by the following equations:

Continued on next page

Weighted linear least-squares equations:
solution of $x_i = a_{i1}y_1 + a_{i2}y_2$

$$y_1 = \frac{1}{d} \sum_{i=1}^{n} b_{1i}x_i$$

$$y_2 = \frac{1}{d} \sum_{i=1}^{n} b_{2i}x_i$$

where

$$w_{ii} = \frac{\text{constant}}{\sigma^2(x_i)}$$

$$c_1 = \sum_{i=1}^{n} w_{ii}a_{i1}{}^2$$

$$c_2 = \sum_{i=1}^{n} w_{ii}a_{i2}{}^2$$

$$c_{12} = \sum_{i=1}^{n} w_{ii}a_{i1}a_{i2}$$

$$d = c_1c_2 - c_{12}{}^2$$

$$b_{1i} = w_{ii}(c_2a_{i1} - c_{12}a_{i2})$$

$$b_{2i} = w_{ii}(c_1a_{i2} - c_{12}a_{i1}) \tag{3.4-3}$$

The linear least-squares equations are often presented in a different form. These refer to the equation

$$Y = MX + C \tag{3.4-4}$$

and values Y_i and X_i are provided to find parameters M and C, the slope and the intercept respectively. It is apparent that $M \equiv y_1$ and $C \equiv y_2$. The values X_i are the values of some controlled variable, like the temperature or a concentration and the values Y_i are the observables. Hence:

$$Y_i \equiv x_i \qquad X_i \equiv a_{i1} \quad \text{and} \quad a_{i2} = 1$$

The appropriate equations can be readily obtained from eqns. (3.4-3) to be as follows:

Weighted linear least-squares equations: solution of $Y = MX + C$

$$M = \frac{1}{d}[(\Sigma\ w_{ii})(\Sigma\ w_{ii}X_iY_i) - (\Sigma\ w_{ii}X_i)(\Sigma\ w_{ii}Y_i)]$$

$$C = \frac{1}{d}[(\Sigma\ w_{ii}X_i{}^2)(\Sigma\ w_{ii}Y_i) - (\Sigma\ w_{ii}X_i)(\Sigma\ w_{ii}X_iY_i)]$$

where

$$d = (\Sigma\ w_{ii}X_i{}^2)(\Sigma\ w_{ii}) - (\Sigma\ w_{ii}X_i)^2$$

$$\Sigma \equiv \sum_{i=1}^{n}$$

$$w_{ii} = \frac{1}{\sigma^2(Y_i)} \qquad (3.4\text{-}5)$$

When the equations are non-linear, the method of least-squares refinement must be used. The calculation starts from initial estimates (guesses) of the parameters y_1 and y_2, which will be given the symbols y'_1 and y'_2. From these estimates values of the observables x'_1, $x'_2, \ldots x'_n$ can be calculated using the known relationship between the observables and the parameters. These values will differ from the experimental ones, both because of experimental error and also because y'_1 and y'_2 are not the best estimates. The differences Δx_i are defined by

$$\Delta x_i = x_i - x'_i \qquad (3.4\text{-}6)$$

From these differences, corrections to the parameters, Δy_1 and Δy_2, can be calculated using the linear least-squares equations. This amounts to an assumption that the relationship between the parameters and observables is linear in the region between the guesses and the best estimates. This will not always be a good assumption, especially if the guesses are a long way off the mark. However, it is likely that the refined parameters, which are $y'_1 + \Delta y_1$ and $y'_2 + \Delta y_2$, will be an improvement on the initial guesses. The refinement process can then be repeated as will be shown below.

To use the linear least-squares equations in this non-linear problem, the coefficients a_{ij} will have to be replaced by the derivatives $(\partial x_i / \partial y_j)$. These derivatives will be usually available as functions of y_1 and y_2.

As the best estimates of the parameters are not available prior to the calculation, the guesses y'_1 and y'_2 must be used to obtain the values of the derivatives.

The equations for obtaining the refinements from the differences are as follows:

Least-squares refinement for two parameters: calculation of the refinements

$$\Delta y_1 = \frac{1}{d} \sum_{i=1}^{n} b_{1i} \Delta x_i$$

$$\Delta y_2 = \frac{1}{d} \sum_{i=1}^{n} b_{2i} \Delta x_i$$

where

$$w_{ii} = \frac{\text{constant}}{\sigma^2(x_i)}$$

$$a_{i1} = \frac{\partial x_i}{\partial y_1}$$

$$a_{i2} = \frac{\partial x_i}{\partial y_2}$$

$$c_1 = \sum_{i=1}^{n} w_{ii} a_{i1}^{2}$$

$$c_2 = \sum_{i=1}^{n} w_{ii} a_{i2}^{2}$$

$$c_{12} = \sum_{i=1}^{n} w_{ii} a_{i1} a_{i2}$$

$$d = c_1 c_2 - c_{12}^{2}$$

$$b_{1i} = w_{ii}(c_2 a_{i1} - c_{12} a_{i2})$$

$$b_{2i} = w_{ii}(c_1 a_{i2} - c_{12} a_{i1}) \qquad (3.4\text{-}7)$$

The refined parameters, $y'_1 + \Delta y_1$ and $y'_2 + \Delta y_2$, are now used as the initial guesses in a further refinement cycle. The cycle is repeated until in most cases (but see below for exceptions) the parameters reach, or very nearly reach, the best estimates. This will happen because, as the parameters become more and more refined, the linear assumption will become more and more nearly valid. This process of convergence to the best estimates is usually monitored by calculating and printing out the weighted sum of the squares of the differences at each cycle. This quantity should decrease uniformly until it reaches a constant value. Theoretically, this can only happen in an infinite number of cycles if the problem is not exactly linear. Some criterion must therefore be chosen for deciding when the convergence has been carried far enough. For example, it could be decided that the convergence is accurate enough when the weighted sum of the squares of the differences falls by less than one per cent between two cycles.

The procedure of least-squares refinement is set out below for easy reference.

Least-squares refinement for two parameters: procedure

---

1. Make initial guesses of parameters: y'_1, y'_2.
2. Calculate the observables x'_i from y'_1, y'_2.
3. Calculate the differences $\Delta x_i = x_i(\text{observed}) - x'_i$.
4. Calculate the weighted sum of the squares of the differences

$$S = \sum_{i=1}^{n} w_{ii}(\Delta x_i)^2$$

5. Is S smaller than its value on the last cycle by more than $S/100$? If yes go to step 10. If no continue with step 6.
6. Calculate the derivatives $(\partial x_i/\partial y_j)$.
7. Calculate the refinements Δy_1 and Δy_2 using eqns. (3.4-7).
8. Set y'_1 equal to $y'_1 + \Delta y_1$ and y'_2 equal to $y'_2 + \Delta y_2$.
9. Go back to step 2.
10. Set y_1 equal to y'_1 and y_2 equal to y'_2.
11. Propagate or calculate errors using relevant equations (see later).

In certain problems least-squares refinement can run into diffi-culties. In this connection it is helpful to think of the problem in terms of a three-dimensional Cartesian diagram in which y'_1 and y'_2 are plotted on the two horizontal axes and the weighted sum of the squares of the differences plotted on the vertical axis. A surface is then obtained in which the lowest point represents the solution according to the principle of least squares. The refinement process then starts on high ground and works its way downhill to reach this minimum point. The shape of this surface can be complex in complex problems and this can lead to difficulties.

Three major problems can arise. Firstly, the refinement process can be very slow if the two values are in a region of the surface which is nearly flat and horizontal. In this case, it may be possible to improve the speed of refinement by starting from a different initial pair of guesses. Secondly, the refinement process may settle on a local minimum, a depression surrounded by higher ground, which is not the true minimum. Sometimes it will be possible to tell that this has happened because the final sum of the squares of the differences is greater than would be expected from the experimental errors. However, in some cases it may not be at all obvious that this has occurred. The way to test for this effect and also to circumvent it if it is known to have occurred, is again to start the refinement from a different initial pair of parameter values. Thirdly, the surface may be such that the refinements overshoot the minimum and the process oscillates for a long time around the best estimates. This can sometimes be avoided by reducing the refinements in each cycle by an arbitrary factor of say 0·5 or 0·1.

If substantial difficulties arise, other parameter-fitting methods should be sought, as mentioned earlier. The advantage of using least-squares refinement, is that some of the quantities calculated in the last cycle of the refinement process can be used in the error analysis, as can be seen later.

3.5 GENERAL ERROR EQUATIONS

In this section general expressions for the variances and the covariance of the parameters y_1 and y_2 are worked out. To derive these expressions it has to be imagined that the process of measuring the n observables and calculating the two parameters from them is repeated N times where N is a very large number, approaching infinity. The variance of y_1 is then given by eqn. (1.2-2) to be

$$\text{var}(y_1) = \frac{1}{N} \sum_{i=1}^{N} ({}^i y_1 - \bar{y}_1) = \frac{1}{N} \sum_{i=1}^{N} {}^i \delta y_1$$

using the notation ${}^i \delta y_1$ introduced in the last chapter.

Using the linear assumption, the equation for ${}^i\delta y_1$ will be analogous to eqn. (3.4-7) for Δy_1, because, even if the least-squares *method* was not used to obtain y_1, the *principle* of least-squares will have been used, ensuring that eqns. (3.4-7) are obeyed. Thus:

$$
{}^i\delta y_1 = \frac{1}{d}\sum_{j=1}^{n} b_{1j}{}^i\delta x_j \tag{3.5-1}
$$

where d and the b_{1j} are given in eqns. (3.4-7). So that in terms of the differences ${}^i\delta x_j$, the variance of y_1 becomes:

$$
\mathrm{var}(y_1) = \frac{1}{d^2 N}\sum_{i=1}^{N}\left(\sum_{j=1}^{n} b_{1j}{}^i\delta x_j\right)^2
$$

When the sum in the bracket is squared, the terms in $({}^i\delta x_j{}^i\delta x_k)$, $k \neq j$ will drop out as they represent covariances of the observables, which are zero in the present problem.

$$
\mathrm{var}(y_1) = \frac{1}{d^2 N}\sum_{i=1}^{N}\sum_{j=1}^{n} b_{1j}{}^2({}^i\delta x_j)^2
$$

$$
= \frac{1}{d^2}\sum_{j=1}^{n} b_{1j}{}^2\,\mathrm{var}(x_j)
$$

$$
= \frac{\sigma^2}{d^2}\sum_{j=1}^{n}\frac{b_{1j}{}^2}{w_{jj}}
$$

using eqn. (3.3-1). Substituting for b_{1j} from eqns. (3.4-7)

$$
\mathrm{var}(y_1) = \frac{\sigma^2}{d^2}\sum_{j=1}^{n} w_{jj}(c_2 a_{j1} - c_{12}a_{j2})^2
$$

$$
= \frac{\sigma^2}{d^2}\left[c_2{}^2\sum_{j=1}^{n} w_{jj}a_{j1}{}^2 + c_{12}{}^2\sum_{i=1}^{n} w_{jj}a_{j2}{}^2\right.
$$

$$
\left. - 2c_2 c_{12}\sum_{j=1}^{n} w_{jj}a_{j1}a_{j2}\right]
$$

$$
= \frac{\sigma^2}{d^2}(c_2{}^2 c_1 - c_{12}{}^2 c_2)
$$

$$
\mathrm{var}(y_1) = \frac{\sigma^2 c_2}{d} \tag{3.5-2}
$$

Similarly

$$\text{var}(y_2) = \frac{\sigma^2 c_1}{d} \tag{3.5-3}$$

The covariance of y_1 and y_2 can be obtained by substituting for $^i\delta y_1$ and $^i\delta y_2$ from eqn. (3.5-1) into the basic eqn. (1.4-1) for the covariance.

$$\text{cov}(y_1, y_2) = \frac{1}{N} \sum_{i=1}^{N} {}^i\delta y_1 {}^i\delta y_2$$

$$= \frac{1}{d^2 N} \sum_{i=1}^{N} \left(\sum_{j=1}^{n} b_{1j} {}^i\delta x_j \right) \left(\sum_{k=1}^{n} b_{2k} {}^i\delta x_k \right)$$

$$= \frac{1}{d^2 N} \sum_{i=1}^{N} \sum_{j=1}^{n} b_{1j} b_{2j} ({}^i\delta x_j)^2$$

In the last line the terms in $({}^i\delta x_j {}^i\delta x_k)$, $j \neq k$ have been dropped, as before, because the observable covariances are zero.

$$\text{cov}(y_1, y_2) = \frac{1}{d^2} \sum_{j=1}^{n} b_{1j} b_{2j} \, \text{var}(x_j)$$

$$= \frac{\sigma^2}{d^2} \sum_{j=1}^{n} \frac{b_{1j} b_{2j}}{w_{jj}}$$

When b_{1j} and b_{2j} are substituted from eqn. (3.4-3)

$$\text{cov}(y_1, y_2) = \frac{\sigma^2}{d^2} \sum_{j=1}^{n} w_{jj}(c_2 a_{j1} - c_{12} a_{j2})(c_1 a_{j2} - c_{12} a_{j1})$$

$$= \frac{\sigma^2}{d^2} \left[c_1 c_2 \sum_{j=1}^{n} w_{jj} a_{j1} a_{j2} - c_2 c_{12} \sum_{j=1}^{n} w_{jj} a_{j1}{}^2 \right.$$

$$\left. - c_1 c_{12} \sum_{j=1}^{n} w_{jj} a_{j2}{}^2 + c_{12}{}^2 \sum_{j=1}^{n} w_{jj} a_{j1} a_{j2} \right]$$

$$= \frac{\sigma^2}{d^2} (c_{12}{}^3 - c_1 c_2 c_{12})$$

$$\text{cov}(y_1, y_2) = -\frac{\sigma^2 c_{12}}{d} \tag{3.5-4}$$

3.6 EQUATIONS FOR ERROR PROPAGATION

We are now imagined to be in the position of having obtained the two parameters from the n observables by some parameter-fitting method using the *principle* of least-squares, which might be the method of least-squares or else some more suitable method. We now wish to obtain the errors in the two parameters and have decided, on the basis of the arguments of Section 3.2, on propagation rather than calculation of errors. It is therefore assumed that we know the variances of x_i and thus we set the weights equal to the inverse of the variances (as must also have been done in the parameter-fitting procedure).

$$w_{ii} = \frac{1}{\mathrm{var}(x_i)}$$

σ^2 is therefore equal to unity in this case.
Equations (3.5-1, 2, 3) then reduce to:

$$\mathrm{var}(y_1) = \frac{c_2}{d}$$

$$\mathrm{var}(y_2) = \frac{c_1}{d}$$

$$\mathrm{cov}(y_1, y_2) = -\frac{c_{12}}{d} \qquad (3.6\text{-}1)$$

These equations are expressed below for practical purposes in terms of the standard deviations and the correlation coefficient.

If the least-squares method has been used to find y_1 and y_2, then c_1, c_2, c_{12} and d will have already been calculated and can be stored ready for the error propagation. If least-squares refinement has been used, then, of course, the values of c_1, etc. to be used will be those calculated in the final cycle.

Continued on next page

Propagation of errors from n observables to two parameters

$$\sigma(y_1) = \left(\frac{c_2}{d}\right)^{\frac{1}{2}}$$

$$\sigma(y_2) = \left(\frac{c_1}{d}\right)^{\frac{1}{2}}$$

$$\rho(y_1, y_2) = -\frac{c_{12}}{(c_1 c_2)^{\frac{1}{2}}}$$

where

$$w_{ii} = \frac{1}{\sigma^2(x_i)}$$

$$a_{i1} = \frac{\partial x_i}{\partial y_1}$$

$$a_{i2} = \frac{\partial x_i}{\partial y_2}$$

$$c_1 = \sum_{i=1}^{n} w_{ii} a_{i1}^{2}$$

$$c_2 = \sum_{i=1}^{n} w_{ii} a_{i2}^{2}$$

$$c_{12} = \sum_{i=1}^{n} w_{ii} a_{i1} a_{i2}$$

$$d = c_1 c_2 - c_{12}^{2} \tag{3.6-2}$$

3.7 EXAMPLE: THE ARRHENIUS PARAMETERS

As an example of error propagation, the standard deviations and correlation coefficient of the two Arrhenius parameters, $A \equiv y_1$ and $E \equiv y_2$ are obtained from the errors in the eight rate constants, $k_1, k_2, \ldots, k_8$, from which the parameters were obtained. These rate constants were obtained experimentally at eight different temperatures, $T_1, T_2, \ldots, T_8$ and are shown in Table 3.1. The basic

TABLE 3.1

ERROR ANALYSIS FOR THE ARRHENIUS PARAMETERS

T_i	k_i	$\sigma(k_i)$	w_{ii}	$\dfrac{\partial k_i}{\partial A} \times 10^8$	$\dfrac{\partial k_i}{\partial E} \times 10^3$	$w_{ii}\left(\dfrac{\partial k_i}{\partial A}\right)^2 \times 10^{15}$	$w_{ii}\left(\dfrac{\partial k_i}{\partial E}\right)^2 \times 10^5$	$w_{ii}\left(\dfrac{\partial k_i}{\partial A}\right)\left(\dfrac{\partial k_i}{\partial E}\right) \times 10^{10}$
280	0·144	0·014	5 102	0·118 918	−0·064 556	7·215 07	2·126 24	−3·916 75
290	0·302	0·030	1 111	0·241 545	−0·126 603	6·482 68	1·780 93	−3·397 82
300	0·589	0·059	287·3	0·467 985	−0·237 112	6·291 58	1·615 12	−3·187 73
310	1·08	0·11	82·64	0·868 829	−0·426 006	6·238 54	1·499 85	−3·058 89
320	2·25	0·23	18·90	1·551 82	−0·737 116	4·552 28	1·027 11	−2·162 33
330	3·56	0·36	7·716	2·675 98	−1·232 57	5·525 38	1·172 25	−2·545 02
340	5·62	0·56	3·189	4·468 94	−1·997 88	6·368 44	1·272 81	−2·847 07
350	8·54	0·85	1·384	7·247 68	−3·147 56	7·270 42	1·371 23	−3·157 44

equation which gives the rate constants in terms of the parameters and temperatures has been given in Section 2.7 to be as follows:

$$k_i = A \exp\left[\frac{-E}{8 \cdot 314 T_i}\right]$$

It simplifies the least-squares calculation if this equation is put in a linear form, making refinement unnecessary.

$$\log_{10} k_i = \log_{10} A - \frac{E}{2 \cdot 303 \times 8 \cdot 314 T_i}$$

Thus if $\log_{10} k_i$ is plotted against $1/T_i$, a straight line is obtained with intercept equal to $\log_{10} A$ and slope proportional to E. This plot is shown in Fig. 3.1 for the example under consideration. The slope and intercept can be calculated using linear least-squares equations in the form of eqns. (3.4-5), once suitable weights have

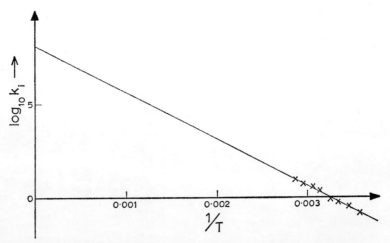

Fig. 3.1   Straight-line relationship used to find the Arrhenius parameters.

been decided on. These experimental rate constants are all believed to have standard deviations of about 10 per cent of their values and these are shown in the third column of Table 3.1. The standard deviations of the $\log_{10} k_i$ will therefore be the same for all eight values, and thus the weights can all be set equal to unity.

From the calculated slope and intercept values of A and E are obtained to be as follows.

$$A = 1 \cdot 26 \times 10^8 \, s^{-1}$$

$$E = 4 \cdot 784 \times 10^4 \, J \, mole^{-1}$$

Because the parameters have been found by this indirect method, the error analysis must start at the beginning by calculating the weights, w_{ii}. These are shown in the fourth column of Table 3.1. The derivatives $\partial k_i / \partial A$ and $\partial k_i / \partial E$ must now be calculated using eqns. (2.7-3). These are shown in the fifth and sixth columns of the table. The final three columns of the table give the terms in the sums for c_1, c_2 and c_{12}. After summation:

$$c_1 = 4 \cdot 994 \, 44 \times 10^{-14}$$

$$c_2 = 1 \cdot 186 \, 55 \times 10^{-4}$$

$$c_{12} = -2 \cdot 427 \, 31 \times 10^{-9}$$

Also

$$d = 3 \cdot 435 \times 10^{-20}$$

From these the standard deviations and correlation coefficient can be determined to be:

$$\sigma(A) = 5 \cdot 9 \times 10^7$$

$$\sigma(E) = 1 \cdot 2 \times 10^3$$

$$\rho(A, E) = 0 \cdot 9971$$

The high value of ρ is typical for data of this type and reflects the comparatively small range of temperature over which the k_i were measured. Conversely, to reduce and improve the standard deviations, the temperature range should be extended. This is not practicable in many cases, however, and one must live with the result that these rate-constant data do not determine E and A independently very well.

The error ellipse for the problem is plotted in Fig. 3.2 showing, as expected, a high degree of correlation. $\sigma(A)$ and $\sigma(E)$ are large, especially $\sigma(A)$, but this does not reflect the true error situation, as the values must be considered in pairs. It is interesting to calculate the conditional standard deviations, *i.e.* the intercepts of this ellipse, using eqns. (2.4-1, 2).

$$\sigma(A, E = 4{\cdot}784 \times 10^4) = 3{\cdot}4 \times 10^5$$
$$\sigma(E, A = 1{\cdot}28 \times 10^8) = 6{\cdot}9$$

The conditional standard deviations are more than two orders of magnitude smaller than the ordinary standard deviations in this case. How they arise in this example is shown diagrammatically in

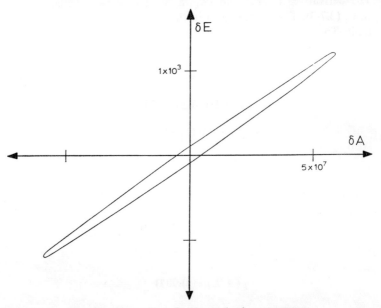

FIG. 3.2   Error ellipse for the Arrhenius parameters.

Fig. 3.3. The plot is a version of that in Fig. 3.1, in which the errors have been exaggerated. The lines labelled 'a' show how the slope and intercept, and therefore also A and E can vary within the errors. However, to have a high value of the intercept (hence high A) one must have at the same time a large negative value of the slope (hence high E), if the line is to keep within the errors of the experimental rate constants. These lines therefore illustrate the ordinary standard deviations and show that there is positive correlation. The lines labelled 'b' both have the same slope and show how A can vary if E is

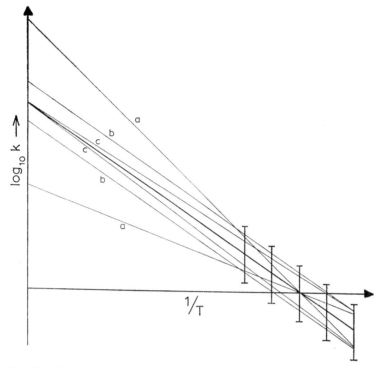

FIG. 3.3   Graph to illustrate the ordinary and conditional standard deviations for the Arrhenius parameters.

kept constant. They illustrate the conditional standard deviation of A. The lines labelled 'c' illustrate the conditional standard deviation of E as the intercept and A are kept constant.

3.8 EQUATIONS FOR ERROR CALCULATION

In this section the errors in the parameters y_1 and y_2 are *calculated* rather than propagated as in Section 3.6. The calculation starts from the observables, $x_1, x_2, \ldots, x_n$, and their assigned weights, $w_{11}, w_{22}, \ldots, w_{nn}$. As the weights are inversely proportional to the variances of the observables, assigning weights is equivalent to deciding on the relative variances of the observables. The methods of Section 1.3 can therefore be used.

Before the error calculation begins, the parameters, y_1 and y_2 are calculated by some method which minimises the weighted sum of the squares of the differences,

$$S = \sum_{i=1}^{n} w_{ii}\varepsilon^2(x_i)$$

S can then be used to find σ^2, the proportionality constant which connects the weights, w_{ii}, and the variances, $\text{var}(x_i)$. The relationship between S and σ^2 is derived as follows.

$$\varepsilon(x_i) = x_i(\text{observed}) - x_i(\text{calculated})$$

$$= \delta x_i - a_{i1}\delta y_1 - a_{i2}\delta y_2$$

where

$$a_{ij} = \frac{\partial x_i}{\partial y_j}$$

The weighted sum can therefore be written:

$$S = \sum_{i=1}^{n} w_{ii}(\delta x_i - a_{i1}\delta y_1 - a_{i2}\delta y_2)^2$$

Expanding:

$$S = \sum_{i=1}^{n} w_{ii}(\delta x_i - a_{i1}\delta y_1 - a_{i2}\delta y_2)\delta x_i$$

$$- \left[\sum_{i=1}^{n} w_{ii}(\delta x_i - a_{i1}\delta y_1 - a_{i2}\delta y_2)a_{i1} \right] \delta y_1$$

$$- \left[\sum_{i=1}^{n} w_{ii}(\delta x_i - a_{i1}\delta y_1 - a_{i2}\delta y_2)a_{i2} \right] \delta y_2 \qquad (3.8\text{-}1)$$

The last two terms in the above equation are both equal to zero; in particular the sums in the square brackets, *i.e.* the coefficients of δy_1 and δy_2 are equal to zero, as will now be shown. As y_1 and y_2 were obtained using the principle of least-squares, δy_1 and δy_2 will be related to the δx_i by the eqns. (3.5-1). These equations can be transformed by straightforward algebraic operations, using also the definition of the coefficients b_{ij} given in eqns. (3.4-7), to give the following relations:

$$(\Sigma w_{ii}a_{i1}a_{i2})\delta y_1 + (\Sigma w_{ii}a_{i2}^2)\delta y_2 = \Sigma w_{ii}a_{i2}\delta x_i$$

$$(\Sigma w_{ii}a_{i1}^2)\delta y_1 + (\Sigma w_{ii}a_{i1}a_{i2})\delta y_2 = \Sigma w_{ii}a_{i1}\delta x_i \qquad (3.8\text{-}2)$$

Further manipulation of the above two equations gives:

$$\Sigma\, w_{ii}(\delta x_i - a_{i1}\delta y_1 - a_{i2}\delta y_2)a_{i1} = 0$$

$$\Sigma\, w_{ii}(\delta x_i - a_{i1}\delta y_1 - a_{i2}\delta y_2)a_{i2} = 0$$

The assertion that the last two terms in eqn. (3.8-1) is thus seen to be proved and

$$S = \sum_{i=1}^{n} w_{ii}(\delta x_i - a_{i1}\delta y_1 a_{i2}\delta y_2)\delta x_i$$

$$= \sum_{i=1}^{n} w_{ii}(\delta x_i)^2 - \sum_{i=1}^{n} w_{ii}a_{i1}\delta x_i\delta y_1 - \sum_{i=1}^{n} w_{ii}a_{i2}\delta x_i\delta y_2$$

Using eqns. (3.5-1) to substitute for δy_1 and δy_2:

$$S = \sum_{i=1}^{n} w_{ii}(\delta x_i)^2 - \sum_{i=1}^{n}\sum_{j=1}^{n} w_{ii}a_{i1}b_{1j}\delta x_i\delta x_j$$

$$- \sum_{i=1}^{n}\sum_{j=1}^{n} w_{ii}a_{i2}b_{2j}\delta x_i\delta x_j \qquad (3.8\text{-}3)$$

The value obtained for S will vary every time a set of observables is obtained. We must imagine now that the sets of observations are made a very large number of times, N, and that on the kth occasion the results ${}^{k}x_i$ are obtained, which give the parameters ${}^{k}y_1$ and ${}^{k}y_2$ and the minimised sum ${}^{k}S$ after a calculation based on the principle of least-squares. If ${}^{k}\delta x_i$, ${}^{k}\delta y_1$ and ${}^{k}\delta y_2$ represent the differences of the quantities obtained on this kth occasion from their respective mean values, then the mean value of S, designated by $\bar{S}$, will be given by

$$\bar{S} = \frac{1}{N}\sum_{k=1}^{N} {}^{k}S$$

$$= \frac{1}{N}\sum_{k=1}^{N}\left[\sum_{i=1}^{n} w_{ii}({}^{k}\delta x_i)^2 - \sum_{i=1}^{n}\sum_{j=1}^{n} w_{ii}a_{i1}b_{1j}{}^{k}\delta x_i{}^{k}\delta x_j\right.$$

$$\left. - \sum_{i=1}^{n}\sum_{j=1}^{n} w_{ii}a_{i2}b_{2j}\delta x_i\delta x_j\right]$$

The terms in $(\delta x_i\delta x_j)$ for $i \neq j$ will be zero since they are proportional to the observable covariances, which are all zero in the present problem. The expression for $\bar{S}$ can therefore be reduced as follows.

$$\bar{S} = \frac{1}{N} \sum_{k=1}^{N} \left[\sum_{i=1}^{n} w_{ii}(^k\delta x_i)^2 - \sum_{i=1}^{n} w_{ii}a_{i1}b_{1i}(^k\delta x_i)^2 \right.$$

$$\left. - \sum_{i=1}^{n} w_{ii}a_{i2}b_{2i}(^k\delta x_i)^2 \right]$$

$$= \sum_{i=1}^{n} w_{ii}\,\mathrm{var}(x_i) - \sum_{i=1}^{n} w_{ii}a_{i1}b_{1i}\,\mathrm{var}(x_i)$$

$$- \sum_{i=1}^{n} w_{ii}a_{i2}b_{2i}\,\mathrm{var}(x_i)$$

Since $w_{ii}\,\mathrm{var}(x_i) = \sigma^2$ for all i,

$$\bar{S} = n\sigma^2 - \sigma^2 \sum_{i=1}^{n} a_{i1}b_{1i} - \sigma^2 \sum_{i=1}^{n} a_{i2}b_{2i} \qquad (3.8\text{-}4)$$

Using the definition of the b_{ij} given in eqns. (3.4-7), it can be easily shown that

$$\sum_{i=1}^{n} a_{i1}b_{1i} = \sum_{i=1}^{n} a_{i2}b_{2i} = 1$$

and hence

$$\bar{S} = \sigma^2(n - 2) \qquad (3.8\text{-}5)$$

Thus, if, as would happen in an actual experimental situation, one set of observations was made, then the quantity $S/(n - 2)$ would give an estimate of σ^2. How good this estimate is likely to be depends, it can be shown, on the value of $(n - 2)$. As indicated in Section 3.2, if $(n - 2)$ is six or greater, the estimate is likely to be a good one in most common situations.

After an estimate of σ^2 has been made, then the variances and the covariance of y_1 and y_2 can be calculated using eqns. (3.5-2, 3, 4). Equations for the standard deviations and correlation coefficient follow and are given below. Again the intermediate quantities c_1, c_2, c_{12} and d and now also S may have been calculated during a least-squares procedure.

Calculation of errors in two parameters, which have been obtained from n observables

$$\sigma(y_1) = \sigma \left(\frac{c_2}{d}\right)^{\frac{1}{2}}$$

$$\sigma(y_2) = \sigma \left(\frac{c_1}{d}\right)^{\frac{1}{2}}$$

$$\rho(y_1, y_2) = -\frac{c_{12}}{(c_1 c_2)^{\frac{1}{2}}}$$

where

w_{ii} is the weight assigned to x_i

S is the weighted sum of the squares of the differences

$$\sigma = \left(\frac{S}{n-2}\right)^{\frac{1}{2}}$$

$$a_{i1} = \frac{\partial x_i}{\partial y_1}$$

$$a_{i2} = \frac{\partial x_i}{\partial y_2}$$

$$c_1 = \sum_{i=1}^{n} w_{ii} a_{i1}^{2}$$

$$c_2 = \sum_{i=1}^{n} w_{ii} a_{i2}^{2}$$

$$c_{12} = \sum_{i=1}^{n} w_{ii} a_{i1} a_{i2}$$

$$d = c_1 c_2 - c_{12}^{2} \tag{3.8-6}$$

3.9 ERROR CALCULATION: EXAMPLE

The rate constant data used in Section 3.7 for propagating errors are used again in this section for calculating errors. The two procedures overlap to some extent, and using the same data serves to illustrate the essential difference.

In the error propagation, the rate constants were all thought to have 10 per cent standard deviations and the weights were calculated accordingly. Here only relative weights need be assigned, but it would be reasonable again to assume a constant (now unknown) percentage error as a basis for choosing weights. Accordingly, the weights used in the error propagation would be suitable. The quantities c_1, c_2, c_{12} and d have therefore already been calculated and the values of Section 3.7 can be used in the present calculation. (If we were starting the procedure from scratch, we would probably use the reciprocal of the squares of the rate constant values as weights, *i.e.* the weights and the values of c_1, etc. would all be greater by a factor of 100. This would not, of course, affect the final result.)

To continue with the error calculation, S must now be calculated using eqn. (3.3-2). This is found to be

$$S = 2 \cdot 599$$

from which

$$\sigma = \left(\frac{S}{6}\right)^{\frac{1}{2}} = 0 \cdot 658$$

This gives values of the standard deviations, using eqns. (3.8-6), of

$$\sigma(A) = 3 \cdot 9 \times 10^7$$

and

$$\sigma(E) = 7 \cdot 9 \times 10^2$$

the value of $\rho(A, E)$ being unchanged. The calculated standard deviations are therefore about 30 per cent less than their propagated values. This indicates that the errors assigned to the rate constant data were probably a little pessimistic.

3.10 ERROR EQUATIONS FOR THE SLOPE AND INTERCEPT

The error propagation eqns. (3.6-2) and calculation eqns. (3.8-6) can be written in a form appropriate to the solution of the straight-line equation $Y = MX + C$. This has already been done for linear least-squares in eqns. (3.4-5). The equations are given below for user convenience.

Propagation of errors to the slope and intercept of $Y = MX + C$

$$\sigma(M) = \left(\frac{\Sigma w_{ii}}{d}\right)^{\frac{1}{2}}$$

$$\sigma(C) = \left(\frac{\Sigma w_{ii}X_i^2}{d}\right)^{\frac{1}{2}}$$

$$\rho(M, C) = -\frac{(\Sigma w_{ii}X_i)}{[(\Sigma w_{ii})(\Sigma w_{ii}X_i^2)]^{\frac{1}{2}}}$$

where $\qquad w_{ii} = \dfrac{1}{\sigma^2(Y_i)}$

$$d = (\Sigma w_{ii}X_i^2)(\Sigma w_{ii}) - (\Sigma w_{ii}X_i)^2$$

$$\Sigma \equiv \sum_{i=1}^{n}$$

n is the number of points

Calculation of errors in the slope and intercept of $Y = MX + C$

$$\sigma(M) = \left(\frac{\Sigma w_{ii}}{d}\right)^{\frac{1}{2}}$$

$$\sigma(C) = \left(\frac{\Sigma w_{ii}X_i^2}{d}\right)^{\frac{1}{2}}$$

$$\rho(M, C) = -\frac{\Sigma w_{ii}X_i}{[(\Sigma w_{ii})(\Sigma w_{ii}X_i^2)]^{\frac{1}{2}}}$$

where $\qquad w_{ii}$ is the weight assigned to y_i

$$d = (\Sigma w_{ii}X_i^2)(\Sigma w_{ii}) - (\Sigma w_{ii}X_i)^2$$

$$S = \Sigma [X_i(\text{observed}) - X_i(\text{calculated})]^2$$

$$\sigma = \left(\frac{S}{n-2}\right)^{\frac{1}{2}}$$

$$\Sigma \equiv \sum_{i=1}^{n}$$

n is the number of points

CHAPTER 4

Error propagation from several observables to the same number of parameters

4.1 LINEAR TRANSFORMATIONS

In this chapter, errors are propagated from any number, n, variables (here called observables) to the same number of new variables (here called parameters). The observables, x_i and the parameters, y_i, are written as column matrices, X and Y:

$$X = \begin{Bmatrix} x_1 \\ x_2 \\ \cdot \\ \cdot \\ \cdot \\ x_n \end{Bmatrix} \qquad Y = \begin{Bmatrix} y_1 \\ y_2 \\ \cdot \\ \cdot \\ \cdot \\ y_n \end{Bmatrix} \qquad (4.1\text{-}1)$$

In most cases it will be possible to write the observables as functions of the parameters:

$$X \equiv X(Y) \qquad (4.1\text{-}2)$$

In some cases, it will be possible to write the parameters as functions of the observables:

$$Y \equiv Y(X) \qquad (4.1\text{-}3)$$

As in Chapter 2, this gives rise to two sets of error propagation equations. Both of these must again be given, although matrix notation considerably condenses the presentation. The two sets of linear equations can be obtained by differentiating (4.1-2) and (4.1-3).

$$dX = A \, dY \qquad (4.1\text{-}4)$$

where

$$A = \begin{cases} \left(\dfrac{\partial x_1}{\partial y_1}, \quad \dfrac{\partial x_1}{\partial y_2}, \quad \cdots, \quad \dfrac{\partial x_1}{\partial y_n}\right) \\[2ex] \dfrac{\partial x_2}{\partial y_1}, \quad \cdots \\[2ex] \cdots \\ \cdots \\[2ex] \left(\dfrac{\partial x_n}{\partial y_1}, \quad \cdots \right) \end{cases}$$

$$dY = B \, dY \qquad (4.1\text{-}5)$$

where

$$B = \begin{cases} \left(\dfrac{\partial y_1}{\partial x_1}, \quad \dfrac{\partial y_1}{\partial x_2}, \quad \cdots, \quad \dfrac{\partial y_1}{\partial x_n}\right) \\[2ex] \dfrac{\partial y_2}{\partial x_1}, \quad \cdots \\[2ex] \cdots \\ \cdots \\[2ex] \left(\dfrac{\partial y_n}{\partial x_1}, \quad \cdots \right) \end{cases} = A^{-1}$$

It is the matrix **B** which is of most direct use in the present problem, but if eqns. (4.1-3) are not available, then it can be obtained by inverting **A**. In the few cases where even eqns. (4.1-2) are not available, **A** must be found by the difference method, using the same calculation procedure that was used to find the parameters themselves, and then inverted to give **B**.

We now use the assumption that the relationship between **X** and **Y** is linear in the region of the errors and write

$$\delta X = A\delta Y \qquad \delta Y = B\delta X \qquad (4.1\text{-}6)$$

where

$$\delta X = X - \overline{X} \qquad \delta Y = Y - \overline{Y}$$

$$\overline{X} = \begin{Bmatrix} \bar{x}_1 \\ \bar{x}_2 \\ . \\ . \\ . \\ \bar{x}_n \end{Bmatrix} ; \qquad \overline{Y} = \begin{Bmatrix} \bar{y}_1 \\ \bar{y}_2 \\ . \\ . \\ . \\ \bar{y}_n \end{Bmatrix}$$

4.2 THE VARIANCE–COVARIANCE MATRIX

The variance–covariance matrix of a set of variables, such as the n observables, x_i, is given the symbol M_x and is defined by:

$$M_x = \begin{Bmatrix} \text{var}(x_1), & \text{cov}(x_1, x_2), & \dots, & \text{cov}(x_1, x_n) \\ \text{cov}(x_2, x_1), & \text{var}(x_2), & \dots & \\ \dots & & & \\ \dots & & & \\ \text{cov}(x_n, x_1), & \dots\dots\dots\dots\dots, & \text{var}(x_n) \end{Bmatrix} \qquad (4.2\text{-}1)$$

The variance–covariance matrix is thus symmetrical. For uncorrelated variables, it is a diagonal matrix. Using the definitions of variance and covariance, *i.e.* eqns. (1.2-2) and (1.4-1), M_x can be written

$$M_x = \frac{1}{N} \sum_{i=1}^{N} {}^i \delta X \, {}^i \delta X' \qquad (4.2\text{-}2)$$

where ${}^i\delta X'$ is the transpose of ${}^i\delta X$ and the superscript i indicates the ith set of observations.

The variance–covariance matrix can also be written in terms of the standard deviations and correlation coefficients.

$$M_x = \begin{pmatrix} \sigma^2(x_1), \ \sigma(x_1)\sigma(x_2)\rho(x_1, x_2), \quad \ldots, \quad \sigma(x_1)\sigma(x_2)\rho(x_1, x_2) \\ \sigma(x_2)\sigma(x_1)\rho(x_2, x_1), \ \sigma^2(x_2), \quad \ldots \\ \ldots \\ \ldots \\ \sigma(x_n)\sigma(x_1)\rho(x_n, x_1), \ldots \ldots \ldots, \quad \sigma^2(x_n) \end{pmatrix}$$

$$(4.2\text{-}3)$$

If we define S_x as a diagonal matrix of standard deviations and R_x as a matrix of correlation coefficients, whose diagonal elements are unity, *i.e.*

$$S_x = \begin{pmatrix} \sigma(x_1), & 0, & 0, & \ldots, & 0 \\ 0, & \sigma(x_2), & 0, & \ldots \\ \ldots \\ \ldots \\ 0, & 0, \ldots \ldots \ldots, & \sigma(x_n) \end{pmatrix} \qquad (4.2\text{-}4)$$

and

$$R_x = \begin{pmatrix} 1, & \rho(x_1, x_2), & \ldots, & \rho(x_1, x_n) \\ \rho(x_2, x_1), & 1, & \ldots \\ \ldots \\ \ldots \\ \rho(x_n, x_1), \ldots \ldots \ldots, & 1 \end{pmatrix} \qquad (4.2\text{-}5)$$

then

$$M_x = S_x R_x S_x \qquad (4.2\text{-}6)$$

4.3 ERROR PROPAGATION EQUATIONS

The problem of propagating errors now becomes one of calculating the variance–covariance matrix for the parameters, M_y, from M_x.

The derivation in matrix notation is a simple one.

$$\mathbf{M}_y = \frac{1}{N} \sum_{i=1}^{N} {}^i\delta\mathbf{Y}^i\delta\mathbf{Y}'$$

$$= \frac{1}{N} \sum_{i=1}^{N} \mathbf{B}^i\delta\mathbf{X}^i\delta\mathbf{X}'\mathbf{B}'$$

$$\mathbf{M}_y = \mathbf{B}\mathbf{M}_x\mathbf{B}' \qquad (4.3\text{-}1)$$

The procedure used therefore, is first to set up the variance–covariance matrix for the observables, the diagonal elements being the observables which must be assigned values in advance of the calculation. The off-diagonal elements are the covariances, which will often be zero. Otherwise, they will have values assigned on the basis of the arguments of Section 1.5. In certain problems $\mathbf{M}_x$ will have a particular pattern. For example, if the observables are points taken off a recorder trace, which is supplied by an amplifier of time-constant equal to the sampling interval, then the correlation matrix will be given by

$$\mathbf{R}_x = \left\{ \begin{array}{llll} 1, & \frac{1}{e}, & \left(\frac{1}{e}\right)^2, & \ldots, & \left(\frac{1}{e}\right)^n \\[2ex] \frac{1}{e}, & 1, & \frac{1}{e}, & \ldots \\[2ex] \left(\frac{1}{e}\right)^2, & \frac{1}{e}, & 1, & \ldots \\[2ex] \cdots \\ \cdots \\ \left(\frac{1}{e}\right)^n, & \ldots\ldots\ldots\ldots, & 1 \end{array} \right\}$$

The variance–covariance matrix will have a similar pattern of elements that are large on the diagonal, falling off in value as the distance from the diagonal increases.

Having obtained $\mathbf{M}_x$ it is then transformed using the matrix of derivatives $\mathbf{B}$. Preferably this is calculated directly: alternatively $\mathbf{A}$ is calculated and inverted. Finally $\mathbf{M}_y$ is analysed to give the standard deviations, $\sigma(y_i)$ and the correlation coefficients, $\rho(y_i, y_j)$, which are often presented in the form of a correlation matrix. The equations are summarised below for easy reference.

Propagation of errors from n observables to n parameters

$$\sigma(y_i) = [(M_y)_{ii}]^{\frac{1}{2}}$$

$$\rho(y_i, y_j) = \frac{(M_y)_{ij}}{\sigma(y_i)\sigma(y_j)}$$

where

$(M_y)_{ij}$ is an element of $\mathbf{M}_y$

$$\mathbf{M}_y = \mathbf{B}\mathbf{M}_x\mathbf{B}'$$

The elements of $\mathbf{B}$ and $\mathbf{M}_x$ are given by

$$(B)_{ij} = \frac{\partial y_i}{\partial x_j}$$

$$(M_x)_{ii} = \sigma^2(x_i)$$

$$(M_x)_{ij} = \sigma(x_i)\sigma(x_j)\rho(x_i, x_j)$$

Alternatively

$$\mathbf{B} = \mathbf{A}^{-1}$$

where

$$(A)_{ij} = \frac{\partial x_i}{\partial y_j} \tag{4.3-2}$$

4.4 PROPAGATION OF ERRORS FROM THREE OBSERVABLES TO THREE PARAMETERS: EXAMPLE

In this example, errors will be propagated from three observables, P_1, P_2 and P_3, to three parameters, p_1, p_2 and p_3. The observables and parameters are linearly related by a transformation matrix, $\mathbf{L}$, thus:

$$\mathbf{P} = \mathbf{L}\mathbf{p}$$

The observables are as follows:

$$\mathbf{P} = \left\{ \begin{array}{c} 243 \\ 23{\cdot}7 \\ -17{\cdot}5 \end{array} \right\}$$

The inverted transformation matrix, L^{-1}, is known to be given by

$$L^{-1} = \begin{Bmatrix} 2\cdot268 & 0\cdot141 & 0\cdot231 \\ -2\cdot474 & -0\cdot394 & 2\cdot214 \\ 0\cdot871 & 4\cdot177 & 0\cdot025 \end{Bmatrix}$$

The parameters can therefore be readily calculated to be

$$P = \begin{Bmatrix} 550 \\ -649 \\ 120 \end{Bmatrix}$$

The first step is to set up M_P. P_1 is thought to have a 1 per cent error, i.e. $\sigma(P_1) = 2\cdot4$. P_2 and P_3 are, however, correlated, as they are obtained from the areas of peaks in a spectrum which overlap (see Section 1.5). Because of the arbitrary separation, P_2 and P_3 are thought to have 5 per cent standard deviations, i.e. $\sigma(P_2) = 1\cdot19$ and $\sigma(P_3) = 0\cdot88$. Were it not for this arbitrary separation, P_2 and P_3 would also have been given 1 per cent standard deviations. It follows that the ratio of the conditional standard deviation to the ordinary standard deviation for these quantities is $0\cdot2$. This corresponds (see Table 2.1) to a correlation coefficient, $\rho(P_2, P_3)$, of $0\cdot98$. M_P can now be set up.

$$M_P = \begin{Bmatrix} 5\cdot76 & 0 & 0 \\ 0 & 1\cdot42 & 1\cdot03 \\ 0 & 1\cdot03 & 0\cdot77 \end{Bmatrix}$$

From this $M_p = L^{-1}M_P(L^{-1})$, can be calculated to be

$$M_p = \begin{Bmatrix} 29\cdot765 & -31\cdot777 & 13\cdot217 \\ -31\cdot777 & 37\cdot453 & -5\cdot191 \\ 13\cdot217 & -5\cdot191 & 29\cdot361 \end{Bmatrix}$$

The standard deviations of the parameters are therefore as follows:

$$\sigma(p_1) = 5\cdot5 \qquad \sigma(p_2) = 6\cdot1 \qquad \sigma(p_3) = 5\cdot4$$

The correlation matrix can now be calculated.

$$R_p = \begin{Bmatrix} 1 & -0\cdot952 & 0\cdot447 \\ -0\cdot952 & 1 & -0\cdot157 \\ 0\cdot447 & -0\cdot157 & 1 \end{Bmatrix}$$

p_1 and p_2 have standard deviations of about 1 per cent because they both depend predominantly on P_1 which has a 1 per cent error. This is also the reason for the high correlation coefficient of -0.952. p_3 has a higher standard deviation since it depends strongly on P_2. The high correlation coefficient between P_2 and P_3 does not carry through to cause high correlation between the p_i's.

4.5 ERRORS IN PREDICTED OBSERVABLES

We now turn to the situation, covered in Section 2.7 for two parameters, in which we have predicted any number of observables, x_i, greater or less in number than the parameters, y_i, and we wish to obtain the errors in the predicted observables.

The starting point is the equation for $\mathbf{M}_x$, which is obtained in an analogous way to eqn. (4.3-1) to give

$$\mathbf{M}_x = \mathbf{A}\mathbf{M}_y\mathbf{A}' \qquad (4.5\text{-}1)$$

The matrix $\mathbf{A}$, *i.e.* the derivatives $(\partial x_i/\partial y_j)$, must be used as $\mathbf{A}$ is not square and does not have an inverse.

The procedure to be used is summarised below. The correlation coefficients between errors in predicted observables are not usually of importance. Only the diagonal elements of $\mathbf{M}_x$ need therefore be calculated:

Propagation of errors from parameters to predicted observables

$$\sigma(x_i) = [(M_x)_{ii}]^{\frac{1}{2}}$$

where

$(M_x)_{ii}$ is a diagonal element of $\mathbf{M}_x$

$\mathbf{M}_x = \mathbf{A}\mathbf{M}_y\mathbf{A}'$

The elements of $\mathbf{A}$ and $\mathbf{M}_y$ are given by

$$(A)_{ij} = \frac{\partial x_i}{\partial y_j}$$

$$(M_y)_{ii} = \sigma^2(y_i)$$

$$(M_y)_{ij} = \rho(y_i, y_j)\sigma(y_i)\sigma(y_j) \qquad (4.5\text{-}2)$$

4.6 PROPAGATION TO FEWER OR MORE PARAMETERS

Sometimes we are not interested in the complete set of parameters. The remaining parameters may not be of particular interest, they may not have any physical significance and, in some cases, it will not be obvious what they are.

It will be possible to calculate only those parameters of interest and their errors provided that firstly it is possible to express the required parameters as functions of the observables. (The 'observables', as can always be the case in this book, may be the parameters from a previous calculation.) Secondly, the parameters must not be overdetermined by the observables. Otherwise all the parameters must be determined using the methods of the next chapter.

In other cases, we will want to propagate errors to a greater number of parameters. Here, the parameters will not all be independent quantities.

In both cases, the procedure to be used is similar to that of Section 4.3, except that the matrix **B** must be used.

Propagation of errors from observables to fewer or more parameters, when the parameters are not overdetermined

$$\sigma(y_i) = [(M_y)_{ii}]^{\frac{1}{2}}$$

$$\rho(y_i, y_j) = \frac{(M_y)_{ij}}{\sigma(y_i)\sigma(y_j)}$$

where $(M_y)_{ij}$ is an element of $\mathbf{M}_y$

and $\mathbf{M}_y = \mathbf{B M}_x \mathbf{B}'$

The elements of $\mathbf{B}$ and $\mathbf{M}_x$ are given by

$$(B)_{ij} = \frac{\partial y_i}{\partial x_j}$$

$$(M_x)_{ii} = \sigma^2(x_i)$$

$$(M_x)_{ij} = \rho(x_i, x_j)\sigma(x_i)\sigma(x_j) \qquad (4.6\text{-}1)$$

4.7 ERRORS IN THE TRANSFORMATION MATRIX

It has been assumed throughout the book so far that errors in the derivatives, *i.e.* in the transformation matrix, are negligible. If this is not the case, then the problem in this chapter becomes essentially one of propagation to fewer parameters, which was discussed in the last section. The procedure to be followed in any problem can be worked out if it is approached from this point of view.

Using this general approach may make the problem rather large and unmanageable, however, and simplification is possible in some cases. Any simplification in procedure should be checked from first principles for each case. As an example, we now discuss the case of n observables and n parameters which are linearly related by

$$\mathbf{Y} = \mathbf{BX}$$

the difference now being that the elements of $\mathbf{B}$ have standard deviations. The elements of $\mathbf{B}$ now count as observables, and the variance–covariance matrix must now include rows and columns for these elements. It will therefore be a square matrix with $n^2 + n$ rows and columns of the following form:

$$\mathbf{M}_{x,b} = \left(\begin{array}{c|c} \mathbf{M}_x & \mathbf{O} \\ \hline \mathbf{O} & \mathbf{M}_b \end{array}\right) \tag{4.7-1}$$

We have assumed here that there is no correlation between errors in the elements of $\mathbf{X}$ and $\mathbf{B}$, which may not always be the case. $\mathbf{M}_y$ will be given by

$$\mathbf{M}_y = \mathbf{J}\mathbf{M}_{x,b}\mathbf{J}' \tag{4.7-2}$$

where

$$\mathbf{J} = \left\{\, \mathbf{B} \,\middle|\, \mathbf{K} \,\right\} \tag{4.7-3}$$

and

$$\mathbf{K} = \left\{\begin{array}{c|c} \begin{array}{c} x_1, x_2, \ldots, x_n \\ \hline \\ \mathbf{O} \end{array} & \begin{array}{c} \mathbf{O} \\ \hline x_1, x_2, \ldots, x_n \\ \hline \mathbf{O} \end{array} \\ & \quad \begin{array}{c} \mathbf{O} \\ \cdots \\ \hline x_1, x_2, \ldots, x_n \end{array} \end{array}\right. \tag{4.7-4}$$

Thus

$$M_y = BM_xB' + KM_bK' \qquad (4.7\text{-}5)$$

i.e. as expected, the elements of M_y are greater than they would be if errors in the elements of B were ignored. Because of the large number of zero elements in K, a complete calculation of KM_bK' is not necessary. In fact the elements of this matrix are given by

$$(KM_bK')_{ij} = \sum_{\substack{k=1 \\ l=1}}^{n} \text{cov}(b_{ik}, b_{jl})x_k x_l \qquad (4.7\text{-}6)$$

Moreover, many of the elements of M_b will be zero in most cases. It is perhaps worth repeating that the procedure to be used should be worked out from first principles for each problem.

CHAPTER 5

Errors in several parameters obtained from many observables

5.1 INTRODUCTION

The equations of Chapter 3 are now extended to any number of parameters using matrix notation, which will allow us to include the procedure for correlated observables quite simply. The full set of n parameters, $y_1, y_2, \ldots, y_n$, are overdetermined by the m observables, $x_1, x_2, \ldots, x_m$, i.e. $m > n$, and the principle of least-squares will have to be used to obtain the least-variance estimates of the parameters. As for the two-parameter case, the least-squares equations are given in Section 5.3.

The question of propagation *versus* calculation of errors will again arise. The arguments of Section 3.2 are relevant here and should be read. Basically, the probability of obtaining a good estimate of the errors from the sum of the squares of the differences depends on the value of $m - n$. If this is six or more, then a good estimate of the errors is likely to be made.

5.2 WEIGHT MATRICES

Both for the error analysis and for the least-squares or other parameter-fitting calculations, weights must be assigned in advance to the observables which should be inversely proportional to the variances (*see* eqn. (3.3-1)). For uncorrelated observables the weights will become the diagonal elements of a weight matrix $\mathbf{W}$:

Continued on next page

The weight matrix for uncorrelated observables

$$\mathbf{W} = \sigma^2 \begin{Bmatrix} \dfrac{1}{\sigma^2(x_1)} & 0 & 0, \ldots \\[2ex] 0 & \dfrac{1}{\sigma^2(x_2)} & 0, \ldots \\[2ex] \cdots & & \\ \cdots & & \\ 0 & 0, \ldots\ldots & \dfrac{1}{\sigma^2(x_m)} \end{Bmatrix} \qquad (5.2\text{-}1)$$

Thus for uncorrelated observables, the weight matrix is inversely proportional to the variance–covariance matrix.

$$\mathbf{W} = \sigma^2 \mathbf{M}_x^{-1} \qquad (5.2\text{-}2)$$

By extension, the weight matrix for correlated variables is defined also as the inverse of the variance–covariance matrix; and, thus defined, proves to be relevant in the error analysis and also the principle of least-squares.

In general, therefore, the weight matrix cannot be shown simply in terms of the standard deviations and correlation coefficients. In the case where there is only one non-zero correlation coefficient (not an uncommon situation) the weight matrix is given by the following procedure:

Setting up the weight matrix if only two of the observables are correlated

If w_{ij} are the elements of $\mathbf{W}$ and only $\rho(x_k, x_l) \neq 0$, then

$$w_{ii} = \frac{\sigma^2}{\sigma^2(x_1)} \quad i \neq k, l$$

$$w_{ij} = 0 \quad i, j \neq k, l$$

$$w_{kk} = \sigma^2 \{\sigma^2(x_k)[1 - \rho^2(x_k, x_l)]\}^{-1}$$

$$w_{ll} = \sigma^2 \{\sigma^2(x_l)[1 - \rho^2(x_k, x_l)]\}^{-1}$$

$$w_{kl} = -\frac{\sigma^2 \rho(x_k, x_l)}{\sigma(x_k)\sigma(x_l)[1 - \rho^2(x_k, x_l)]}$$

$$w_{lk} = w_{kl} \qquad (5.2\text{-}3)$$

If there is more than one off-diagonal element, then the situation becomes more complex and cannot be described concisely here. However, often simplified procedures can be developed to suit particular cases, which do not involve inverting the whole variance–covariance matrix. In general, the point can be made that, if only some of the observables are correlated, or if they are correlated in groups, then the weight matrix can be arranged in diagonal blocks, which can be inverted separately. And the reader should be reminded that these matrices are symmetric, for which more rapid computation procedures are available than for more general matrix inversion.

The least-squares principle for uncorrelated observables was given in Section 3.3. The sum to be minimised, S, is given by eqn. (3.3-2). In matrix notation, this equation becomes

$$S = E'WE \qquad (5.2\text{-}4)$$

where W is the weight matrix for uncorrelated observables and E is a column matrix of the differences:

$$E = \begin{pmatrix} \varepsilon(x_1) \\ \varepsilon(x_2) \\ \cdot \\ \cdot \\ \cdot \\ \varepsilon(x_n) \end{pmatrix} \qquad (5.2\text{-}5)$$

Equation (5.2-4) can be extended to define S for correlated observables, i.e. when W has off-diagonal elements. If this is done, it can be shown that the principle of least-squares, i.e. that S should be minimised to obtain the best estimates of the parameters, applies also to correlated observables.

5.3 LEAST-SQUARES EQUATIONS AND REFINEMENT

The equations for linear least-squares are first obtained. In this case, the observables depend linearly on the parameters thus:

$$X \text{ (calculated)} = AY \qquad (5.3\text{-}1)$$

If Y is a column matrix of parameters which are the best estimates obtained using the principle of least squares, then

$$E = X - AY$$

and

$$S = (X - AY)'W(X - AY)$$

For a minimum value of S, $(\partial S/\partial y_i)$ must be zero for all values of i:

$$\frac{\partial S}{\partial y_i} = (X - AY)'W(-A_i) + (-A_i)'W(X - AY)$$

$$= 0 \qquad (i = 1, 2, \ldots, m) \tag{5.3-2}$$

where A_i is a column matrix which is the ith column of A. The two terms in eqn. (5.3-2) are the transpose of one another and, as they are scalar quantities, they are identical and are both equal to zero:

$$A'_i W(X - AY) = 0 \tag{5.3-3}$$

Putting the terms on the left-hand side of eqn. (5.3-3) into a column matrix and setting it equal to zero:

$$A'W(X - AY) = 0$$

Hence

$$A'WAY = A'WX \tag{5.3-4}$$

Equations (5.3-4) are referred to as the 'normal equations' in matrix form. They can be solved for the best estimates of the parameters.

Linear least-squares equations: solutions of $X = AY$

$$Y = (A'WA)^{-1}A'WX \tag{5.3-5}$$

where W is the weight matrix (*see* Section 5.2).

For situations where the dependence of X on Y is not linear, least-squares refinement must be used. The calculation starts from initial guesses of the parameters which will be designated by $\hat{Y}$. From these values of the calculated observables, $\hat{X}$, are obtained. If we define Δ matrices by

$$\Delta_x = X - \hat{X} \qquad \Delta_y = Y - \hat{Y}$$

where X are the measured values of the observables and Y the best estimates of the parameters. We now assume that Δ_x and Δ_y are small enough so that the relationship between them is approximately linear and the linear least-squares equations can be used to find Δ_y from Δ_x. The elements of A will now be $(\partial x_i / \partial y_j)$ and as these are usually available as functions of Y, $\hat{Y}$ will have to be used to obtain them approximately. The equations for obtaining the refinements are as follows:

Least-squares refinement: calculation of the refinements

$$\Delta_y = (A'WA)^{-1} A'W\Delta_x$$

where W is the weight matrix (*see* Section 5.2) and the elements of A are given by

$$(A)_{ij} = \frac{\partial x_i}{\partial y_j} \qquad (5.3\text{-}6)$$

The refined parameters $\hat{Y} + \Delta_y$ are now used as the initial guesses in a further refinement cycle. As in the two-parameter case, refinement is continued until S reaches a fairly constant value, *e.g.* it may be decided that the refinement will end if S falls by less than one per cent of its value after one refinement cycle. The least-squares refinement procedure is summarised below.

The problems that can arise with least-squares refinement are those that were discussed briefly in Section 3.4 for the two-parameter case, although they are likely to be greater in degree for more parameters.

Continued on next page

Least-squares refinement procedure

1. Make initial guesses of the parameters, $\hat{\mathbf{Y}}$.
2. Calculate the observables, $\hat{\mathbf{X}}$, from $\hat{\mathbf{Y}}$.
3. Calculate the differences, $\Delta_x = \mathbf{X} - \hat{\mathbf{X}}$.
4. Calculate the weighted sum of the squares of the differences, $S = \Delta'_x \mathbf{W} \Delta_x$.
5. Is S smaller than its value on the last cycle by more than (say) $S/100$? If yes, go to step 10. If no, continue with step 6.
6. Calculate the derivatives $(\partial x_i / \partial y_j)$.
7. Calculate the refinements Δ_y using eqns. (5.3-6).
8. Set $\hat{\mathbf{Y}}$ equal to $\hat{\mathbf{Y}} + \Delta_y$.
9. Go back to step 2.
10. Set $\mathbf{Y}$ equal to $\hat{\mathbf{Y}}$.
11. Propagate or calculate errors using relevant equations (*see later*).

5.4 GENERAL ERROR EQUATIONS

A general expression for the variance–covariance matrix of the parameters will now be derived. We must imagine that the complete set of observations is made a very large number, N, times and that on the ith occasion, parameters $^i\mathbf{Y}$ are obtained by some method based on the principle of least-squares. Then if $\overline{\mathbf{Y}}$ are the mean values of the parameters obtained after the N observations and

$$^i\delta\mathbf{Y} = {}^i\mathbf{Y} - \overline{\mathbf{Y}}$$

then the variance–covariance matrix for the parameters will be given by

$$\mathbf{M}_y = \frac{1}{N} \sum_{i=1}^{N} {}^i\delta\mathbf{Y}^i\delta\mathbf{Y}'$$

We make the usual assumption that $^i\delta\mathbf{X}$ and $^i\delta\mathbf{Y}$ are linearly related over the range of the errors, in which case $^i\delta\mathbf{Y}$ can be expressed by equations of the form of (5.3-6), *i.e.*

$$^i\delta\mathbf{Y} = (\mathbf{A}'\mathbf{W}\mathbf{A})^{-1}\mathbf{A}'\mathbf{W}^i\delta\mathbf{X}$$

Thus, as the matrices $\mathbf{W}$ and $(\mathbf{A}'\mathbf{W}\mathbf{A})^{-1}$ are symmetric, $\mathbf{M}_y$ is given by

$$\mathbf{M}_y = \frac{1}{N} \sum_{i=1}^{N} (\mathbf{A}'\mathbf{W}\mathbf{A})^{-1}\mathbf{A}'\mathbf{W}^i\delta\mathbf{X}^i\delta\mathbf{X}'\mathbf{W}\mathbf{A}(\mathbf{A}'\mathbf{W}\mathbf{A})^{-1}$$

$$= (\mathbf{A}'\mathbf{W}\mathbf{A})^{-1}\mathbf{A}'\mathbf{W}\mathbf{M}_x\mathbf{W}\mathbf{A}(\mathbf{A}'\mathbf{W}\mathbf{A})^{-1}$$

But, since

$$M_x W = \sigma^2 I_m$$

where I_m is a unit matrix of rank m,

$$M_y = \sigma^2 (A'WA)^{-1} \qquad (5.4\text{-}1)$$

This is the basic equation that is used to obtain M_y. It is equivalent to

$$M_y = (A'M_x^{-1}A)^{-1} \qquad (5.4\text{-}2)$$

which shows how the variance–covariance matrix must be transformed in a least-square situation. When the parameters are not overdetermined, A is a square matrix and eqn. (5.4-2) simplifies to eqn. (4.3-1).

5.5 EQUATIONS FOR ERROR PROPAGATION

The situation for error propagation is that the standard deviations and correlation coefficients of the observables are known in advance. The weight matrix used is then the inverse of the variance–covariance matrix and $\sigma^2 = 1$. Equation (5.4-1) is used and the procedure is summarised below.

Propagation of errors from m observables to n overdetermined parameters

$$\sigma(y_i) = [(M_y)_{ii}]^{\frac{1}{2}}$$

$$\rho(y_i, y_j) = \frac{(M_y)_{ij}}{[\sigma(y_i)\sigma(y_j)]}$$

where

$$M_y = (A'WA)^{-1}$$

$$W = M_x^{-1}$$

and the elements of A and M_x are given by

$$(A)_{ij} = \frac{\partial x_i}{\partial y_j}$$

$$(M_x)_{ii} = \sigma^2(x_i)$$

$$(M_x)_{ij} = \rho(x_i, x_j)\sigma(x_i)\sigma(x_j) \qquad (5.4\text{-}3)$$

If a linear least-square calculation has been done, then $(A'WA)^{-1}$ will have already been calculated. If a least-squares refinement has been done, then $(A'WA)^{-1}$ from the final cycle should be used.

5.6 PROCEDURE FOR ERROR CALCULATION

To set up the weight matrix for an error *calculation*, only the relative variances of the observables need be known. Any correlation coefficients which are not zero must also be assigned (absolute) values. The variance–covariance matrix for the observables can then be set up to within an arbitrary, unknown constant factor, σ^2. The weight matrix can then be obtained by inversion, applying the short-cuts, described in Section 5.2, where appropriate.

The parameters, Y, will have again been obtained by some method using the principle of least-squares. The weighted sum of the squares of the differences, S, should also be obtained. From S, σ^2 can be obtained as follows:

$$S = E'WE$$

Now

$$E = X - AY = \delta X - A\delta Y$$

Therefore

$$S = (\delta X - A\delta Y)'W\delta X - (\delta X - A\delta Y)'WA\delta Y$$

The second term in the above equation is equal to zero, since δY was obtained using the principle of least-squares it will therefore obey an equation of the form of (5.3-6), *i.e.*

$$A'WA\delta Y = A'W\delta X \tag{5.6-1}$$

Transposing both sides of this equation gives

$$\delta Y'A'WA = \delta X'WA$$

which is equivalent to

$$(\partial X - A\delta Y)'W\delta X = 0$$

The second term in the equation for S can therefore be dropped.

$$S = (\delta X - A\delta Y)_i W\delta X$$

$$= \delta X'W\delta X - \delta Y'A'W\delta X$$

$$= \delta X'W\delta X - \delta Y'(A'WA)\delta Y$$

$$S = \text{Tr}\,\{\delta X\delta X'W\} - \text{Tr}\,\{\delta Y\delta Y'(A'WA)\}$$

If a very large number of sets of observations are made, then a mean value of S, designated by $\bar{S}$, will be obtained.

$$\bar{S} = \sum_{i=1}^{N} [\text{Tr}\,\{^i\delta X^i \delta X'W\} - \text{Tr}\,\{^i\delta Y^i \delta Y'(A'WA)\}]$$

$$= \text{Tr}\,\{M_x W\} - \text{Tr}\,\{M_y(A'WA)\}$$

$$= \sigma^2\,\text{Tr}\,\{I_m\} - \sigma^2\,\text{Tr}\,\{I_n\}$$

$$\bar{S} = \sigma^2(m - n)$$

If, as is normal, one set of observations is made, then $S/(m - n)$ gives an estimate of σ^2, the reliability of which depends, as indicated earlier, on the value of $(m - n)$. Having obtained a value for σ^2, M_y can be obtained using eqn. (5.4-1). Introducing a convenient matrix

$$P = (A'WA)^{-1}$$

the procedure can be outlined below.

Calculation of errors in n parameters that are overdetermined by m observables

---

$$\sigma(y_i) = \sigma[(P)_{ii}]^{\frac{1}{2}}$$

$$\rho(y_i, y_j) = \frac{(P)_{ij}}{[(P)_{ii}(P)_{jj}]^{\frac{1}{2}}}$$

where

$(P)_{ij}$ are the elements of P and

$$P = (A'WA)^{-1}$$

W is an appropriate weight matrix

$$\sigma = \left(\frac{E'WE}{m - n}\right)^{\frac{1}{2}}$$

$$E = X(\text{observed}) - X(\text{calculated})$$

and the elements of A are given by

$$(A)_{ij} = \frac{\partial x_i}{\partial y_j}$$

If a least-squares calculation has been done, $\mathbf{P}$ will have been computed. $(\mathbf{E'WE})$ may have been calculated also. In a least-squares refinement, values of these quantities are obtained from the last cycle.

5.7 ERROR CALCULATION: AN EXAMPLE

In this example, nine observables, z_i, are fitted to the equation

$$z(c) = \frac{1 + sc}{t + uc}$$

to obtain the parameters s, t and u. The nine values of c and z are given in Table 5.1, columns 1 and 2. From these the following parameters were obtained by least-squares refinement.

$$s = 7 \cdot 7 \qquad t = 14 \cdot 5 \qquad u = 4 \cdot 3$$

Much of the error calculation was in fact done as part of the refinement process, but the steps in the error analysis will be recapitulated here. It is felt, firstly, that the standard deviations of all the z_i are likely to be equal and also that the z_i are uncorrelated. A unit matrix of rank 9 can therefore be used for the weight matrix. $\mathbf{A}$ should now be calculated, the elements of which are given by

$$a_{i1} = \frac{\partial z_i}{\partial s} = \frac{c_i}{t + uc}$$

$$a_{i2} = \frac{\partial z_i}{\partial t} = -\frac{1}{(t + uc_i)^2}$$

$$a_{i3} = \frac{\partial z_i}{\partial u} = -\frac{c_i}{(t + uc_i)^2}$$

Numerical values for these elements are given in Table 5.1. The last three columns of this table thus form the matrix $\mathbf{A}$.

The matrix $\mathbf{A'WA} = \mathbf{A'A}$ is now calculated to be

$$\mathbf{A'A} = \left\{ \begin{array}{ccc} 0 \cdot 099\ 531 & -0 \cdot 003\ 552 & -0 \cdot 012\ 924 \\ -0 \cdot 003\ 552 & 0 \cdot 000\ 177 & 0 \cdot 000\ 437 \\ -0 \cdot 012\ 924 & 0 \cdot 000\ 437 & 0 \cdot 001\ 692 \end{array} \right\}$$

TABLE 5.1

ERROR CALCULATION EXAMPLE

c_i	z_i	$\partial z_i/\partial s \times 10^{-2}$	$\partial z_i/\partial t \times 10^{-3}$	$\partial z_i/\partial u \times 10^{-3}$
0·35	0·080	2·186 6	−4·963 6	−1·737 2
0·60	0·084	3·513 5	−5·026 8	−3·016 1
1·00	0·097	5·322 4	−5·032 3	−5·032 3
2·00	0·108	8·669 9	−4·797 5	−9·594 9
3·00	0·124	10·969 7	−4·451 6	−13·354 9
4·00	0·129	12·647 1	−4·104 6	−16·418 6
4·50	0·132	13·326 4	−3·941 4	−17·736 3
5·00	0·138	13·924 7	−3·786 6	−18·933 8

After inversion

$$\mathbf{P} = \begin{Bmatrix} 7613 & 25\,313 & 51\,593 \\ 25\,313 & 99\,765 & 167\,516 \\ 51\,593 & 167\,516 & 351\,286 \end{Bmatrix}$$

The quantity $S = \mathbf{E}'\mathbf{W}\mathbf{E}$ is here simply the sum of the squares of the differences.

$$S = 2\cdot85 \times 10^{-5}$$

Thus

$$\sigma = \left(\frac{S}{6}\right)^{\frac{1}{2}} = 2\cdot18 \times 10^{-3}$$

The variances can now be obtained by multiplying the square roots of the elements of $\mathbf{P}$ by σ.

$$\sigma(s) = 1\cdot9 \qquad \sigma(t) = 0\cdot7 \qquad \sigma(u) = 1\cdot3$$

The correlation matrix can also be calculated from $\mathbf{P}$ to be as follows.

$$\mathbf{R} = \begin{Bmatrix} 1 & 0\cdot92 & 0\cdot998 \\ 0\cdot92 & 1 & 0\cdot89 \\ 0\cdot998 & 0\cdot89 & 1 \end{Bmatrix}$$

5.8 ERRORS IN THE TRANSFORMATION MATRIX

When the parameters are overdetermined, errors in the transformation matrix are dealt with in the following way. As in Section 4.7, the quantities that give rise to errors have to be counted as observables. However, in this section, they must also be included in the list of parameters, since, in an error propagation or calculation when the parameters are overdetermined, the full set of parameters must be used. Using these principles, the procedure for any particular problem can be worked out.

APPENDIX A

Bibliography

The books listed below all cover a fairly wide range of material in the field of applied statistics, but include to some extent the subject matter of the present volume. Of these, the books by Hamilton and by Arley and Buch present multivariate error analysis and least-squares in the most accessible form, whilst that by Hald covers the two-parameter problem in some detail.

ACTON, F. S., *Analysis of Straight-line Data*, John Wiley and Sons, Inc., New York, 1959.

ARLEY, N. and BUCH, K. R., *Introduction to the Theory of Probability and Statistics*, John Wiley and Sons, Inc., New York, 1950.

BROWNLEE, K. A., *Statistical Theory and Methodology in Science and Engineering*, John Wiley and Sons, Inc., New York, 1965.

FISHER, R. A., *Statistical Methods for Research Workers*, Oliver and Boyd, Edinburgh, 1970.

GRAYBILL, F. A., *An Introduction to Linear Statistical Models*, Vol. 1, McGraw-Hill Book Co., Inc., New York, 1961.

HALD, A., *Statistical Theory With Engineering Applications*, John Wiley and Sons, Inc., New York, 1950.

HAMILTON, W. C., *Statistics in Physical Science*, Ronald Press Co., New York, 1964.

APPENDIX B

Computer procedures

B.1 INTRODUCTION

Computer program segments are given in this section which can be used to carry out all the types of multivariate error analysis covered in this book. In many cases it will be preferable to write tailor-made procedures, but even in these cases, the following examples may prove instructive.

Two procedures are given: one for error propagation, called *errprop*; and one for error calculation, called *errcalc*. The two segments are given in both Algol and Fortan.

Errprop can be used in situations where the number of parameters, n, is the same as, exceeds or is less than the number of observables, m. It must be supplied with the standard deviations of the observables and also the correlation coefficients, if any of the observables are correlated. It must also be supplied with one of the sets of derivatives $\partial x_i/\partial y_j$ or $\partial y_i/\partial x_j$, *i.e.* one of the matrices **A** or **B**. If the numbers of observables and parameters are equal, then either set of derivatives

TABLE B.1

POSSIBLE USES OF ERRPROP

	$n = m$	$n > m$	$n < m$
Option 1: using $\partial x_i/\partial y_j$ derivatives	Straightforward propagation	Calculation not valid	Parameters overdetermined by observables
Option 2: using $\partial y_i/\partial x_j$ derivatives	Straightforward propagation	Parameters not all independent	Parameters not a complete set

84

may be supplied. If not, then the set of derivatives to be supplied is dictated by the circumstances. This question has been discussed earlier in the book and is summarised in Table B.1.

Errcalc must always be used in a situation where the parameters are overdetermined by the observables and have been calculated using the principle of least-squares. Derivatives are not required. Instead a procedure or subroutine must be supplied by the user, which will calculate the set of observables from the parameters. *Errcalc* is thus suitable for use with some of the common parameter-fitting procedures.

B.2 ERRPROP: USER'S NOTES
The Algol procedure and Fortran subroutine are introduced by the following statements respectively.

procedure errprop(no,n,m,sigma,rho,aorbtr,fail);

SUBROUTINE ERRPROP(NO,N,M,SIGMA,RHO,
AORBTR,*)

The dummy parameters are replaced as follows when the procedure or subroutine is called.

NO   is the option number. If NO is replaced by 1, the derivatives $\partial x_i/\partial y_j$ (the matrix **A**) are used. If NO is replaced by 2, the derivatives $\partial y_i/\partial x_j$ (the matrix **B**) are used.
N   is the number of parameters.
M   is the number of observables.
SIGMA   is a one-dimensional array, which should initially contain the standard deviations of the observables and which will finally contain those of the parameters.
RHO   is a one-dimensional array in which the upper triangle of the correlation matrices, including the diagonal elements, are stored by rows. Initially, it should contain the correlation matrix of the observables. If, however, the observables are all uncorrelated, the user may instead set the first element of RHO equal to zero. Finally the array will contain the parameter correlation coefficients.

AORBTR   is a two-dimensional array containing either the matrix **A** or the transpose of **B**, consistent with the value given to NO.

Fail   should be replaced by a label through which the pro-
or *   cedure will exit if it fails for any of the following reasons.
(*i*) If any of the observable standard deviations, supplied by the user, are zero or negative.
(*ii*) If the first element of RHO is neither 0 nor 1.
(*iii*) If the correlation matrix supplied by the user is not a positive definite matrix (as it must be by definition). This means that the correlation matrix has been incorrectly supplied or else was incorrectly estimated. In the latter case it is probable that the magnitude of one or more of the off-diagonal elements has been set too high.
(*iv*) If the procedure calculates a zero value for one of the parameter standard deviations. This will usually be because the matrix **A** or **B** has been wrongly supplied.

The dimensions of SIGMA, RHO and AORBTR should be as follows.

SIGMA   N or M, whichever is the greater.
RHO $N(N+1)/2$ or $M(M+1)/2$, whichever is the greater.
AORBTR   M,N or N,N whichever is the greater.

Attention must be paid to the DIMENSION and LOGICAL statements inside the Fortran subroutine.

B.3 ERRPROP: ALGOL LISTING

procedure errprop(no,n,m,sigma,rho,aorbtr,fail);

integer no,n,m; array sigma,rho,aorbtr; label fail;

begin real bigajj,type,x; integer i,j,k,kk,mm,nn;

     for i: = 1 step 1 until m do

     if sigma[i]$\leq$0 then goto fail;

     type := rho[1];

if type = 0 then goto s1 else

if type = 1 then goto s3 else goto fail;

s1: if no = 2 then goto s2;

for i: = 1 step 1 until m do sigma[i] := 1/sigma[i];

s2: for i: = 1 step 1 until m do sigma[i] := sigma[i]↑2;

k := 0;

for i: = 1 step 1 until n do

for j: = i step 1 until n do

begin k := k+1; rho[k] := 0;

for kk: = 1 step 1 until m do

rho[k] := rho[k] + sigma[kk]*aorbtr[kk,i]*aorbtr[kk,j]

end;

goto s5;

s3: k := 0;

for i: = 1 step 1 until m do

for j: = i step 1 until m do

begin k := k+1;

rho[k] := rho[k]*sigma[i]*sigma[j]

end;

if no = 1 then goto s6;

```
s4:    for i:=1 step 1 until n do

       begin for j:=1 step 1 until m do

              begin sigma[j] := 0;

                     for k:=1 step 1 until m do

                            begin if k≥j then kk := ((2*m−j)*(j−1))/2 + k

                                   else kk := ((2*m−k)*(k−1))/2 + j;

                                   sigma[j] := sigma[j] + aorbtr[k,i]*rho[kk]

                     end

              end;

              for j:=i step 1 until n do

              begin x := 0;

                     for k:=1 step 1 until m do

                     x := x + sigma[k]*aorbtr[k,j];

                     aorbtr[j,i] := x

              end

       end;

       k := 0;

       for i:=1 step 1 until n do

       for j:=i step 1 until n do

       begin k := k+1; rho[k] := aorbtr[j,i] end;
```

type := 0;

s5:   if no = 2 then goto s7;

s6:   nn := (if type = 1 then m else n);

      begin array p,q[1 :nn]; boolean array r[1 :nn];

      for i: = 1 step 1 until nn do r[i] := true;

      for i: = 1 step 1 until nn do

      begin bigajj := 0; kk := 1;

          for j: = 1 step 1 until nn do

          begin if r[j] and abs(rho[kk]) > bigajj then

              begin bigajj := abs(rho[kk]);

                  k := j; mm := kk

          end;

              kk := kk + nn − j + 1

      end;

      if bigajj = 0 then goto fail;

      kk := k; r[k] := false;

      q[k] := 1/rho[mm]; p[k] := 1; rho[mm] := 0;

      for j: = 1 step 1 until k − 1 do

      begin p[j] := rho[kk]; rho[kk] := 0;

          kk := kk + nn − j;

```
                q[j] := q[k]*(if r[j] then −p[j] else p[j])
        end;

        kk := ((2*nn−k)*(k−1))/2;

        for j:=k+1 step 1 until nn do

        begin p[j] := if r[j] then rho[kk+j] else −rho
                                                [kk+j];

                q[j] := −rho[kk+j]*q[k]; rho[kk+j] := 0
        end;


        kk := 1;

        for j:=1 step 1 until nn do

        for k:=j step 1 until nn do

                begin rho[kk] := rho[kk]+p[j]*q[k]; kk := kk+1
                                                        end
    end

  end;

  if type=1 then goto s4;

s7:  j := 1;

  for i:=1 step 1 until n do

  begin if rho[j]≤0 then goto fail;

        sigma[i] := sqrt(rho[j]);

        rho[j] := 1;

        j := j+n−i+1
```

end;

k := 0;

for i:=1 step 1 until n−1 do

begin k := k+1;

    for j:=i+1 step 1 until n do

    begin k := k+1;

        rho[k] := rho[k]/(sigma[i]*sigma[j])
    end

end

end errprop;

B.4 ERRPROP: FORTRAN LISTING

```
SUBROUTINE ERRPROP(NO,N,M,SIGMA,RHO,
                                   AORBTR,*)

DIMENSION SIGMA(10),RHO(55),AORBTR(10,10),P(10),
                                         Q(10)

LOGICAL R(10)

DO 1 I=1,M

IF(SIGMA(I)) 2,2,3

1   CONTINUE

2   RETURN 1

3   TYPE = RHO(1)−1

IF(TYPE) 4,10,2
```

4   GO TO (5,7),NO

5   DO 6 I=1,M

6   SIGMA(I) = 1/SIGMA(I)

7   DO 8 I=1,M

8   SIGMA(I) = SIGMA(I)**2

     K = 0

     DO 9 I=1,N

     DO 9 J=I,N

     K = K+1

     RHO(K) = 0

     DO 9 L=1,M

9   RHO(K) = RHO(K) + SIGMA(L)*AORBTR(L,I)*
                                                AORBTR(L,J)
     GO TO 18

10   K = 0

     DO 11 I=1,M

     DO 11 J=I,M

     K = K+1

11   RHO(K) = RHO(K)*SIGMA(I)*SIGMA(J)

     GO TO (19,12),NO

12   DO 16 I=1,N

```
      DO 15 J=1,M

      SIGMA(J) = 0

      DO 15 K=1,M

      IF(K-J) 13,14,14

13    L = ((2*M-K)*(K-1))/2 + J

      GO TO 15

14    L = ((2*M-J)*(J-1))/2 + K

15    SIGMA(J) = SIGMA(J) + AORBTR(K,I)*RHO(L)

      DO 16 J=I,N

      X = 0

      DO 38 K=1,M

38    X = X + SIGMA(K)*AORBTR(K,J)

16    AORBTR(J,I) = X

      K = 0

      DO 17 I=1,N

      DO 17 J=I,N

      K = K+1

17    RHO(K) = AORBTR(J,I)

      TYPE = -1

18    GO TO (19,34),NO
```

```
19   IF(TYPE) 20,21,2

20   NN = N

     GO TO 22

21   NN = M

22   DO 23 I=1,NN

23   R(I) = .TRUE.

     DO 33 I=1,NN

     BIGAJJ = 0

     L = 1

     DO 25 J=1,NN

     IF(R(J).AND.ABS(RHO(L)).GT.BIGAJJ) GO TO 24

     GO TO 25

24   BIGAJJ = ABS(RHO(L))

     K = J

     MM = L

25   L = L+NN-J+1

     IF(BIGAJJ) 26,2,26

26   L = K

     R(K) = .FALSE.

     Q(K) = 1/RHO(MM)
```

```
     P(K) = 1

     RHO(MM) = 0

     IF(K - 1) 29,29,27

27   DO 28 J=1,K-1

     P(J) = RHO(L)

     RHO(L) = 0

     L = L+NN-J

     Q(J) = Q(K)*P(J)

28   IF(R(J)) Q(J) = -Q(J)

29   L = ((2*NN-K)*(K-1))/2

     IF(NN-K) 32,32,30

30   DO 31 J=K+1,NN

     P(J) = -RHO(L+J)

     IF(R(J)) P(J) = -P(J)

     Q(J) = -RHO(L+J)*Q(K)

31   RHO(L+J) = 0

32   L = 1

     DO 33 J=1,NN

     DO 33 K=J,NN

     RHO(L) = RHO(L) + P(J)*Q(K)
```

```
33   L = L+1

     IF(TYPE) 34,12,2

34   J = 1

     DO 36 I=1,N

     IF(RHO(J)) 2,2,35

35   SIGMA(I) = SQRT(RHO(J))

     RHO(J) = 1

36   J = J+N-I+1

     K = 0

     DO 37 I=1,N-1

     K = K+1

     DO 37 J=I+1,N

     K = K+1

37   RHO(K) = RHO(K)/(SIGMA(I)*SIGMA(J))

     RETURN

     END
```

B.5 ERRCALC: USER'S NOTES
The Algol procedure and Fortran subroutine are introduced by the following statements respectively.

```
     procedure errcalc(no,n,m,x,y,sigma,worrho,calfun, fail);
     SUBROUTINE ERRCALC(NO,N,M,X,Y,SIGMA,
                                      WORRHO,CALFUN,*)
```

The dummy parameters are replaced as follows when the procedure or subroutine is called.

NO   is the option number. If NO is replaced by 1, no weights need be supplied by the user and the procedure assumes that all the observables have been given equal weights in the parameter-fitting procedure. If NO is replaced by 2, weights for each observable, *i.e.* the diagonal elements of the weight matrix, must be supplied by the user in the first M elements of the array WORRHO. The procedure assumes that the off-diagonal elements of the weight matrix are zero. If NO is replaced by 3, the whole upper triangle of the weight matrix, must be stored in rows in the array WORRHO before the procedure or subroutine is called.

N   is the number of parameters.

M   is the number of observables.

X   is a one-dimensional array which should contain the measured values of the observables.

Y   is a one-dimensional array which should contain values of the parameters, which have been obtained using the principle of least-squares and the same weights that are stored in WORRHO.

SIGMA   is a one-dimensional array which will contain the standard deviations of the parameters after the procedure has been called.

WORRHO   is a one-dimensional array which should initially contain the weight matrix, as indicated earlier. Finally it will contain the upper triangle of correlation matrix of the parameters, including the diagonal elements, stored in rows.

CALFUN   is a procedure or subroutine which must be supplied by the user. It should be introduced by a statement of the form of procedure calfun(x,y) or SUBROUTINE CALFUN(X,Y) and should be written to calculate the observables, x or X, from supplied values of the parameters, y or Y.

Fail or *   should be replaced by a label through which the procedure will exit if it fails for any of the following reasons.

(*i*) If the value of N supplied is greater than that of M.

(*ii*) If any of the parameters supplied are zero.

(*iii*) If the weight matrix supplied by the user under option 3 is not a positive definite matrix (as it must be by definition). This means that the weight matrix has been wrongly supplied or estimated. In the latter case it is probable that the magnitude of one or more of the off-diagonal elements has been set too high.

(*iv*) If, by some remote chance, the procedure calculates a zero value for one of the parameter standard deviations.

The dimensions of the arrays should be as follows.

X	M
Y	N
SIGMA	N
WORRHO	If NO=1 then $N(N+1)/2$. If NO=2 then M or $N(N+1)/2$, whichever is the greater. If NO=3 then $M(M+1)/2$.

Attention must be paid to the DIMENSION and LOGICAL statements inside the Fortran subroutine.

B.6 ERRCALC: ALGOL LISTING

```
procedure errcalc(no,n,m,x,y,sigma,worrho,calfun,fail);

integer no,n,m; array x,y,sigma,worrho;

procedure calfun; label fail;

begin real bigajj,s; integer i,j,k,kk,ii,mm; switch s1 = ss1,ss2,ss3;

    array p,q[1:m],a[1:m,1:n]; boolean array r[1:n];

    if n≥m then goto fail;

    calfun(p,y);

    for i:=1 step 1 until n do
```

begin if y[i]=0 then goto fail;

    y[i] := y[i]*1.00001;

    calfun(q,y);

    y[i] := y[i]*0.99999;

    for j:=1 step 1 until m do

    a[j,i] := (q[j]−p[j])*100000/y[i]

end;

for i:=1 step 1 until m do q[i] := p[i]−x[i];

s := 0; k := 0; goto s1[no];

ss1: for i:=1 step 1 until m do s := s = q[i]↑2;

    s := s/(m−n);

    for i:=1 step 1 until n do

    for j:=i step 1 until n do

    begin k := k+1; worrho[k] := 0;

        for kk:=1 step 1 until m do

        worrho[k] := worrho[k] + a[kk,i]*a[kk,j];

        worrho[k] := worrho[k]/s

    end;

    goto ss4;

ss2: for i :=1 step 1 until m do s := s + q[i]↑ 2*worrho[i];

```
s := s/(m−n);

for i:=1 step 1 until n do

begin for j:=i step 1 until n do

        begin p[j] := 0;

                for kk:=1 step 1 until m do

                p[j] := p[j] + worrho[kk]*a[kk,i]*a[kk,j]

        end;

                for j:=i step 1 until n do a[j,i] := p[j]

end;

for i :=1 step 1 until n do

for j :=i step 1 until n do

begin k := k+1; worrho[k] := a[j,i]/s end;

goto ss4;

ss3:    for i:=1 step 1 until m do

for j:=i step 1 until m do

begin k := k+1;

        s := s + (if i=j then worrho[k]*q[i]↑2

        else 2*worrho[k]*q[i]*q[j]

end;

s := s/(m−n);
```

```
for i: = 1 step 1 until n do

begin for j: =i step 1 until n do

      begin p[j] := 0;

            for k: = 1 step 1 until m do

            for kk: = 1 step 1 until m do

            begin ii := (if k≥kk then ((2*m−kk)*(kk−1))/
                                                    2 + k

                  else ((2*m−k)*(k−1))/2 + kk;

                  p[j] := p[j] + a[k,i]*a[kk,j]*worrho[ii]

            end

      end;

      for j: =i step 1 until n do a[j,i] := p[j]

end;

k := 0;

for i: = 1 step 1 until n do

for j: =i step 1 until n do

begin k := k+1; worrho[k] := a[j,i]/s end;
```
ss4:   ```for i: = 1 step 1 until n do r[i] := true;```
```
for i: = 1 step 1 until n do

begin bigajj := 0; kk := 1;

      for j: = 1 step 1 until n do
```

```
begin if r[j] and abs(worrho[kk]) > bigajj then

    begin bigajj := abs(worrho[kk]);

        k := j; mm := kk

    end;

    kk := kk+n-j+1

end;

if bigajj=0 then goto fail;

kk := k; r[k] := false; q[k] := 1/worrho[mm];

p[k] := 1; worrho[mm] := 0;

for j:=1 step 1 until k-1 do

begin p[j] := worrho[kk]; worrho[kk] := 0;
                                    kk := kk+n-j;

        q[j] := q[k]*(if r[j] then -p[j] else p[j])

end;

kk := ((2*n-k)*(k-1))/2;

for j:=k+1 step 1 until n do

begin p[j] := if r[j] then worrho[kk+j]

        else -worrho[kk+j];

        q[j] := -worrho[kk+j]*q[k];

        worrho[kk+j] := 0

end;
```

```
kk := 1;

for j:=1 step 1 until n do

for k:=j step 1 until n do

begin worrho[kk] := worrho[kk]+p[j]*q[k];

        kk := kk+1

end

end;

j := 1;

for i :=1 step 1 until n do

begin if worrho[j]≤0 then goto fail;

    sigma[i] := sqrt(worrho[j]);

    worrho[j] := 1; j := j+n−i+1

end;

k := 0;

for i:=1 step 1 until n−1 do

begin k := k+1;

    for j:=i+1 step 1 until n do

    begin k := k+1;

        worrho[k] := worrho[k]/(sigma[i]*sigma[j])

    end
```

```
        end

end errcalc;
```

B.7 ERRCALC: FORTRAN LISTING

```
SUBROUTINE ERRCALC(NO,N,M,X,Y,SIGMA,
                              WORRHO,CALFUN,*)

DIMENSION X(10),Y(10),SIGMA(10),WORRHO(55),
2              P(10),Q(10),A(10,10)

LOGICAL R(10)

IF(M − N) 2,2,3

2    RETURN 1

3    CALL CALFUN(P,Y)

     DO 5 I=1,N

     IF(Y(I)) 4,2,4

4    Y(I) = Y(I)*1.00001

     CALL CALFUN(Q,Y)

     Y(I) = Y(I)*0.99999

     DO 5 J=1,M

5    A(J,I) = (Q(J) − P(J))*100000/Y(I)

     DO 6 I=1,M

6    Q(I) = X(I) − P(I)
```

```
       S = 0

       K = 0

       GO TO (7,11,16),NO

  7    DO 8 I=1,M

  8    S = S + Q(I)**2

       S = S/(M-N)

       DO 10 I=1,N

       DO 10 J=I,N

       K = K + 1

       WORRHO(K) = 0

       DO 9 L=1,M

  9    WORRHO(K) = WORRHO(K) + A(L,I)*A(L,J)

 10    WORRHO(K) = WORRHO(K)/S

       GO TO 25

 11    DO 12 I=1,M

 12    S = S + Q(I)**2*WORRHO(I)

       S = S/(M-N)

       DO 14 I=1,N

       DO 13 J=I,N

       P(J) = 0
```

```
      DO 13 L=1,M

13    P(J) = P(J) + WORRHO(L)*A(L,I)*A(L,J)

      DO 14 J=I,N

14    A(J,I) = P(J)

      DO 15 I=1,N

      DO 15 J=I,N

      K = K+1

15    WORRHO(K) = A(J,I)/S

      GO TO 25

16    DO 19 I=1,M

      DO 19 J=I,M

      K = K+1

      IF(J−I) 2,17,18

17    S = S + WORRHO(K)*Q(I)**2

      GO TO 19

18    S = S + 2*WORRHO(K)*Q(I)*Q(J)

19    CONTINUE

      S = S/(M−N)

      DO 23 I=1,N

      DO 22 J=I,N
```

P(J) = 0

DO 22 K=1,M

DO 22 L=1,M

IF(K−L) 21,21,20

20   II = ((2*M−L)*(L−1))/2 + K

GO TO 22

21   II = ((2*M−K)*(K−1))/2 + L

22   P(J) = P(J) + A(K,I)*A(L,J)*WORRHO(II)

DO 23 J = I,N

23   A(J,I) = P(J)

K = 0

DO 24 I=1,N

DO 24 J=I,N

K = K+1

24   WORRHO(K) = A(J,I)/S

25   DO 26 I=1,N

26   R(I) = .TRUE.

DO 36 I=1,N

BIGAJJ = 0

L = 1

```
      DO 28 J=1,N

      IF(R(J).AND.ABS(WORRHO(L)).GT.BIGAJJ) GO TO 27

      GO TO 28

27    BIGAJJ = ABS(WORRHO(L))

      K = J

      M = L

28    L = L+N-J+1

      IF(BIGAJJ) 29,2,29

29    L = K

      R(K) = .FALSE.

      Q(K) = 1/WORRHO(M)

      P(K) = 1

      WORRHO(M) = 0

      IF(K-1) 32,32,30

30    DO 31 J=1,K-1

      P(J) = WORRHO(L)

      WORRHO(L) = 0

      L = L+N-J

      Q(J) = Q(K)*P(J)

31    IF(R(J)) Q(J) = -Q(J)
```

32   L = ((2*N−K)*(K−1))/2

      IF(N−K) 35,35,33

33   DO 34 J=K+1,N

      P(J) = −WORRHO(L+J)

      IF(R(J)) P(J) = −P(J)

      Q(J) = −WORRHO(L+J)*Q(K)

34   WORRHO(L+J) = 0

35   L = 1

      DO 36 J=1,N

      DO 36 K=J,N

      WORRHO(L) = WORRHO(L) + P(J)*Q(K)

36   L = L+1

      J = 1

      DO 38 I=1,N

      IF(WORRHO(J)) 2,2,37

37   SIGMA(I) = SQRT(WORRHO(J))

      WORRHO(J) = 1

38   J = J+N−I+1

      K = 0

      DO 39 I=1,N−1

```
      K = K+1

      DO 39 J=I+1,N

      K = K+1

39    WORRHO(K) = WORRHO(K)/(SIGMA(I)*SIGMA(J))

      RETURN

      END
```

Index